Enjoy in Peace
Al Chamberlin
12.4.00

CIRCLE OF COURAGE

CIRCLE OF COURAGE

Al Chamberlin

VANTAGE PRESS
New York • Los Angeles

FIRST EDITION

Copyright © 1991 by Al Chamberlin

Published by Vantage Press, Inc.
516 West 34th Street, New York, New York 10001

Manufactured in the United States of America
ISBN: 0-533-09092-X

Library of Congress Catalog Card No.: 90-90127

3 4 5 6 7 8 9 0

*To the heroes
of the Second Platoon
of L Company,
179th Infantry,
45th Divison*

Foreword

Reading the manuscript of *Circle of Courage* made it seem like only yesterday that a boyish, lanky second lieutenant was introduced to us as the platoon leader of the Second Platoon, L Company, 179th Infantry Regiment of the 45th Division. There he stood, GI-issue green towel around his neck like a scarf, tucked under his fatigues jacket lapels. Two daggers, one in each boot, made us feel uneasy about what we might be in for. More often than not those that created "hero" images were the first to crack under the strains of combat. This was not the case with Lieutenant Chamberlin. He was every bit the superior combat officer, as he would soon demonstrate in the battles on Eerie, T-bone and Baldy.

Circle of Courage brought back fond memories of my many brave comrades in combat. I feel a kinship with them that runs deep. I applaud and thank Al Chamberlin for telling the truth about the fierce fighting that we went through and how most of us were cheated out of our medals.

—Robert Browne

Preface

One might wonder why I chose to write *Circle of Courage*, an account of my tour of duty in Korea with myself as the leading character. I did not do it to eulogize myself. I have already received my awards. Rather, I wrote it to set the record straight about what my men went through in Korea, their courageous heroism in battle and the great injustice done to them by not awarding them the medals they were recommended for and so richly deserved. Many other veterans may well have had the same experience.

The trigger that set my pen in motion was a request from one of my heroes, Bob Browne, to go to bat for him again in another attempt to get his medals from the bureaucratic military establishment. Again we were unsuccessful, even with the help of his congressman.

The Army claimed there was no record of the recommendations in his record. Somehow the written eyewitness accounts of his acts of heroism had been lost or destroyed. I rewrote the recommendations and the witnesses rewrote their accounts but the Army did nothing. Perhaps they were too busy giving medals to "heroes" of Grenada and Panama.

So *Circle of Courage* was written to reassure Bob and the other heroes of the Second Platoon, and to tell their friends, that they really had been recommended for and were deserving of the medals listed on the last page of my book.

Acknowledgments

I would like to thank the following people for providing valuable input for my book:

James Baker
Robert Browne
William Browne
James Crimmins
Harry Cottrell
Mansell Garrett
Jack Neathery
William West
and my daughter, Judy Joy Csicsatka

CIRCLE OF COURAGE

1

They had been told it stunk but they were not prepared for such a stink. It was worse than the smell of shit.

Japan had stunk too, but not as badly as this. As a matter of fact, the smells of Japan had become sweeter with each day there. They had been safe in Japan and every day they had remained there meant one more day of safety. And if any had minded the smells of the Japanese countryside or villages, they need not have left the military replacement depot, cleaned and scrubbed to American standards by Japanese laborers. But even for those who did leave the base for whatever purpose—the search for souvenirs, the gaiety of the cabarets, or perhaps merely to relieve pent-up passions in geisha houses—the smells of Japan soon became tolerable. The aroma of human excreta applied amply to the rice paddies and vegetable gardens became less offensive with each passing.

The Japanese women who toiled in them, often with babies strapped to their backs and sometimes up to their bosoms in water, appeared immune to the odor. For some Americans with farm backgrounds, it was perhaps nostalgic of sweetly manured fields back home. And the smells of the narrow, dusty streets did not excessively offend the experienced adventurer, except perhaps the open fish markets with seafood that had been exposed too long to the hot summer sun, or the honey carts that regularly collected human fertilizer from homes and business establishments. These were filled by busy little natives running from house to house in their peculiar half-run, half-walk gait. They seemed unperturbed by the smell of the job. Two honey buckets dangled from each end of a yoke-like piece of equipment balanced on their shoulders. From the receptacles in the houses, to the honey buckets to the honey carts, to the paddies and gardens, went this useful waste. It stunk mostly when stirred in passage. The clean, perfumed scents of the geisha houses were probably the sweetest aromas of Japan. At least they had been to Second Lieutenant Al Chamberlin.

But now the smells of Japan were behind them as they crossed the Sea of Japan from Sasebo to Pusan. Some would have said it was the stench of shit that now violated the ocean and permeated the air for miles out to sea. But no one word could adequately describe the putrid stink of Pusan. It seemed to be a combination of all the offensive odors in the world, from the past, present, and even the future, all rolled into one all-enveloping atmosphere. The body odors of the men on the deck of the ship were nothing in comparison.

Was there included the smell of fear? Or did fear stimulate the senses so that the stink was sharper? Chamberlin wondered if he would ever get used to the smell. He also wondered if he was afraid. But he had to go to Korea—not just because he had been ordered to, but because he demanded it of himself. He could not explain this obsession. It had nothing to do with patriotism, though he believed in what his country was fighting for. He would have been disappointed to have been assigned to a unit in Japan like some of the replacements had been. Even the few days he had spent at the replacement depot had been restless ones for him. In order to maintain his physical and psychological equilibrium while waiting, he had made a few trips to the geisha houses. He had spent the rest of his spare time exercising, keeping his equipment in good order, and sleeping. He wanted to be ready when the test of combat came.

Maybe that was it. Maybe he had to prove he was a man. Perhaps this had been his goal all his twenty-seven years. Certainly it had motivated him earlier in life. He remembered how his father had always called him puny and weak. Who was weak now? The old bastard was in a hospital in Burlington, Vermont, recuperating from rectal surgery. His father always claimed he had been 4F during World War I. He, himself, had also been 4F at age eighteen in February of 1943. This similarity with his father had been hard to take. But he passed the physical six months later and went into the Army.

He could not wait to get into a combat outfit and go into combat. He would have been disappointed if the war had ended too soon for realization of this personal goal. As it was, his outfit, the 303rd Infantry, had barely made it into combat at the tail end of the war in Germany. They were there just long enough for him to earn two battle stars, the Combat Infantryman Badge, and the bronze star that went with it. As far as he knew he had conducted himself with reasonable courage. He had been scared a few times and had a few close calls, but this apparently had not satisfied his need to prove his manhood. He had not killed anybody that he knew of. He now had a strong urge to stick an enemy with his bayonet. That would prove something. Perhaps that he was sick.

Of course he could rationalize this obsessive need to prove himself in combat. He now planned on making a

3

career of the military, after not knowing what to do with a Latin major when he had graduated from Syracuse University in 1951. He had joined ROTC in his junior year and got his commission when he graduated. He knew how important it was for promotions to get combat experience, earn campaign ribbons and battle stars. But like all rationalizations, this one probably fell short of the truth also.

The stink grew stronger as they approached Pusan. Most of the men, mostly second lieutenants—for that was what was needed most in Korea—became more bitchy and restless.

"What a stinking place," said Second Lieutenant Bill Brownly. "These people must live like pigs."

"Yeah, what a fucking place to be sent to," agreed Second Lieutenant George Goodboy. "Why couldn't we have been sent to Hokkaido instead of this godforsaken hellhole? Some guys get all the breaks."

"Oh, I don't know," mused Chamberlin. "We'll probably get used to the smell."

"I hope I don't get stuck with a rifle platoon," worried Brownly. "A mortar platoon wouldn't be too bad. At least then you're not right on the front lines."

"I don't think I could handle a rifle platoon either," said Goodboy. "How about you, Al?"

The three stood at the ship's rail watching the gray silhouette of Korea draw near. They had attended the Officers Associate Course at Fort Benning together and knew each other well. Now the three of them had been assigned to the 45th Division in Korea.

"I don't know, George," replied Al. "That's what we're supposed to be trained for, but I guess I have my fears, too."

After they had landed and were settled in their bil-

4

lets and had had chow, the three friends took a stroll down through Pusan.

Soon they were approached by a young, dirty little pimp. "Hey, GI, want pretty flower girl? Only ten dollars. Good piece. Come on. I show you."

He grabbed Brownly's hand. Brownly withdrew his hand and cringed away. "We don't want any girls," he said. "Leave us alone."

Brownly was a virgin and he intended to stay that way, at least while in Korea. He wanted to look for souvenirs to send to his mother as future evidence of his having been in such a far away, exotic place. Goodboy was no virgin but he was not about to have anything to do with Korean prostitutes. The Orientals reminded him too much of animals. He could not see lowering himself to relationships with them. Besides, they had heard that Korean prostitutes were loaded with VD, and that many of them were connected with Communist guerrillas. Brownly and Goodboy were interested only in the wares of the dusty little shops that lined the narrow streets.

But Chamberlin had different ideas. He was married, with a pregnant wife back home, but being sexually faithful to her was a value he had long since discarded. He gave it little thought. He knew that sooner or later, if he lived long enough, he would want a piece of ass so badly that he would not worry whether it was Korean or not. And he had long lost any desire for masturbation. So why wait? In fact, topping off the first day in Korea this way seemed intriguing to him.

"Maybe you like sucka hachi?" continued the pimp persistently. "Me number one sucka hachi boy. Only five dollars. Come on."

"We don't want anything like that," said Goodboy. "We're just looking for souvenirs. Don't bother us."

"You like cherry? I let you fuck my sister. She number one cherry girl. I know. I fuck her myself."

"Go on. Get. Leave us alone." Brownly was very indignant.

"Wait," suggested Chamberlin. "Let's talk to him."

"Are you kidding?" asked Goodboy with surprise. "I don't want to get VD off a prostitute or a knife in the back."

"If we stick together we'll be all right. And I've got some pro kits with me, just in case."

"You go ahead if you want to," said Goodboy. "We'll wait for you up the street."

The little boy took Chamberlin's hand and started leading him down an alley.

"Wait a minute," ordered Chamberlin. "How much?"

"Twenty dollars. Number one cherry girl. You fuck two times."

"Oh, no. I give you two dollars." Chamberlin knew well what the going rate was. He had spent six months in Japan after World War II as well as the last few days. Why should it be any more in Korea, he thought.

"Maybe five dollars?"

"Two dollars."

"Okay."

The little, straight-haired, dirty-faced, barefoot boy led Chamberlin on down the alley. They entered a house after Chamberlin had removed his boots. The pimp turned Chamberlin over to a man and went out into the streets again in search of more customers. The man escorted Chamberlin down a narrow stairway. Chamberlin's right hand tightened on his M2 carbine. Then the realization that his boots had been placed alongside other GI boots reassured him. He felt a little

6

foolish. But still, maybe they were boots of dead soldiers. A blond, blue-eyed American lad stepped out of one of the small, thinly partitioned cubicles where the girls worked and smiled at him. Chamberlin guessed things were okay.

The man pointed Chamberlin toward a door and held out his hand. Chamberlin gave him two dollars and stepped through the door. It was the smallest fucking place he had ever seen, not more than four by six. Good thing he was only six foot one. Along one wall on the straw floor was a narrow, quilted pad. On the floor at one end of the pad was the remainder of the girl's equipment, a box of Kleenex and a jar of Vaseline.

The girl was young and plain, but not unattractive. She was not in the least coquettish.

"Come on," she said, as she slipped out of her scanty shift and assumed an unimaginative position on the pad, with her legs spread and drawn up so that her feet were flat on the pad next to her buttocks. "Let's go."

Chamberlin did not like such a direct, matter-of-fact approach to sex, but for two dollars what could he expect? And she was probably a busy girl. Besides, he could not keep his buddies waiting too long. He set his piece in a corner and stripped for action.

The action did not take long. The girl was not the greatest, nor was she the worst. There was nothing special about the sex—just a release of normal, uninhibited maleness for him; a living for her.

When he was finished Chamberlin used the government-issue pro kit as prescribed. The girl cleaned herself with a Kleenex in preparation for her next customer.

Chamberlin rejoined his companions and they returned to their billets. Chamberlin slept well that night.

Brownly tossed and turned. He wondered what

"sucka hachi" meant. He thought he knew but would never dare to admit it. He wondered if that was what the little boy had done. He also wondered if Chamberlin had done it to the boy's sister. For some reason he thought of the sister as being younger and smaller than the boy. *Would Chamberlin do that?* Chamberlin was older and had earned a Combat Infantryman Badge in World War II, something Brownly thought worthy of respect. He had looked up to Chamblin before. But now he wondered what kind of a man he was. Was he sick? What a sordid world! His eyes moistened as he thought of his dear mother. How he wished he was back at her side again. These darn army cots were so narrow. It was difficult for him to curl up in his normal fetal position.

2

From Pusan they moved on up through the replacement pipeline. Looking out the windows of a snail-paced troop train, they saw the Korean peasants hard at work in their rice paddies, their heads protected from the hot summer sun by cone-shaped, straw hats. Wizened-faced little old men carried heavy loads along dusty roads. They balanced these on A-frames which were strapped to their backs. These were three-pronged crotches cut from trees of the right size and shape to fit the back. The upward pointing prongs often cradled burdens of much greater weight than the bearer. Long logs, firewood, building material, bundles of produce, or personal belongings were carried in this manner by the men. However, the Korean women usually carried their loads in baskets balanced on their heads. The men bent forward under their loads; the women stood straight. Most of the men seen were old. Young men were in the war. Dirty-faced, ragged, barefoot, chattering kids held out grubby hands for handouts when the train pulled into stations. Natives grinned as the Americans disembarked briefly to urinate in front of them.

After a brief stop at Division Headquarters, Lieutenants Brownly, Goodboy, and Chamberlin continued by jeep toward the 38th parallel and the front lines. A dusty ride took them to the Command Post of the 3rd Battalion, 179th Infantry Regiment. Along the way they had seen the sheer steepness of mountains they had skirted. They had heard tales of the rugged slopes from Korean veterans. Now they had seen them. Soon they would know them.

"Sir, there are three new officers here," a sergeant reported to Lieutenant Colonel Spottswood, the Battalion Commander.

"Send them in one at a time," ordered Spottswood.

Brownly reported smartly to the colonel. Spottswood returned his salute lazily and looked him over quizzically. Brownly was a tall, fairly slim lad of twenty-two years. His outstanding feature, an oval baby face, belied his age. The pinkish glow of smooth cheeks, with their blond peach fuzz just beginning to stiffen, made him look even younger.

This is what they send me to put in charge of battle-hardened troops, thought Spottswood sadly. No wonder there were so many leadership problems on the platoon level. He did not know whether to feel more sorry for the men whom this young officer would lead into battle or for the young lad himself.

"Do you think you can lead a platoon of men?" he asked pointedly, but not unkindly.

"Yes, Sir. I was especially good with mortars in training. I understand the principles of mortar fire control extremely well, Sir." Brownly was not the least bit modest in his bid for the safest possible combat assignment.

"It just so happens that there is an opening in M Company for a mortar platoon leader. So I'll assign you there."

"What did you get?" asked Goodboy anxiously as Brownly came out.

"The mortar platoon," said Brownly excitedly, "just what I wanted."

Goodboy reported to the Colonel. He was a more mature-looking man than Brownly. Thinning dark hair topped a round, dark-complected face, made darker by a day's shadow of thick stubble. He was not very tall but looked strong and confident.

One look at him and Spottswood thought, a rifle platoon for you, lad. But the Colonel always gave a new replacement a chance to air his choice. "What kind of an assignment would you like, Lieutenant?" he asked.

Goodboy had a theory. Ask for the worst and you are more apt to get the best.

"I would like to be a rifle platoon leader," he said simply. He had wanted it to sound like he was really gung ho, but it had not come out that way at all.

"Fine, I'll assign you to I Company. They need some new blood up there." Actually Spottswood had no choice. There were no other openings left except rifle platoon leaders. Safer positions were usually filled quickly by veterans. Brownly had just lucked out in getting the mortar platoon.

That knocks that theory all to hell, thought Goodboy, as he walked out of the tent.

"Don't try to outfox him," he mumbled to Chamberlin when he came out.

Chamberlin stepped into the command tent and saluted Spottswood smartly. He looked much younger than his twenty-seven years. He was a tall, slim officer with piercing blue eyes. A Combat Infantryman Badge adorned the left breast of his fatigue jacket. He had been glad when he had noticed that it was common for soldiers in Korea to wear the Combat Infantryman Badge and their rank on their uniforms. In World War II, that would have been unheard of. Officers' insignia or noncommissioned officers' stripes made good targets for

11

snipers—evidence, perhaps, that World War II had been more dangerous than the Korean Police Action. Something else to be happy about.

"I see you've been in combat before, Lieutenant. Is this your second tour in Korea?" Somehow Chamberlin did not look old enough to have been in the big war.

"No, Sir. I was in World War II."

"What outfit?"

"The 97th Infantry Division in Germany, Sir."

"What was your MOS?"

"I was a machine gunner, Sir."

"Do you think you can lead a rifle platoon?"

"I don't know, Sir. I think I could lead a machine-gun platoon better, Sir."

"Sorry, son, but we don't need a machine-gun platoon leader right now. But L Company needs officers pretty badly. They can use a man with experience."

After the three new replacements had left, each on his separate way, the colonel remained behind his field desk in deep thought.

Spottswood was a man of average size. Silver hair, thinning with age, capped a fair-complected face. A furrowed forehead spoke of many military campaigns, not all of which he had escaped unscathed. Pale blue eyes softened an already kind face. One the right collar of his clean, well-pressed fatigue jacket was the silver oak leaf designating his rank. On the left collar were the crossed rifles of the Infantry. The Combat Infantryman Badge, with a stainless steel star connecting the top ends of the wreath signifying combat action in two wars, decorated the left breast.

Spottswood thought about his latest three platoon leaders. Brownly will probably be all right as a mortar platoon leader, he mused silently. It was easy to dismiss

12

him from his thoughts. But something about Goodboy bothered him, something sinister. So many young platoon leaders had been wasted in this senseless struggle. Would he be another one?

His wife had recently sent him an article about the West Point class of 1950. He thought about Lieutenant Pierce, the commander of L Company. Pierce was a graduate of that ill-fated class. There was one other, Major Clark, the son of General Mark Clark. Major Clark was now an instructor at Fort Benning after having been wounded and decorated for gallantry in action in Korea. Two officers remaining alive from a class of 670 fine young men, the cream of American youth. What a waste! He forced his thoughts out of the pits of pessimistic premonitions about Goodboy. But it was difficult because Pierce also sparked dire ideas of death, something akin to the eerie sensation prompted by Goodboy.

Now Chamberlin—there was something different about him. He could not put his finger on it. Maybe it was the fact that, like himself, he had seen combat in World War II. He wondered if he had ever been wounded, as he had. Maybe it was the fair complexion and blue eyes, like his. Probably not. Brownly also had those features and he had not felt the same chemical kinship with him. Maybe that was it. Kinship. Chamberlin could well have been his son. Someday he would like to talk to him some more. He hoped to get the chance. Somehow he felt he would. It was an inexplicably warm feeling that did not lend itself to rationality. Maybe that was why he had sent him to L Company. Pierce was still alive and he wanted him to stay that way. He might need all the help he could get. He had sensed an aura of protectiveness about Chamberlin.

First Lieutenant James Pierce greeted Chamberlin

warmly but with no great excitement. Pierce was not a tall man, nor was he heavyset. But he did not appear small either. Perhaps it was his broad shoulders, square jaw, and heavy thighs evidenced by tight-fitting fatigue pants, thighs you would expect to see on a football running back, that made him appear strong and rugged. He wore his silver lieutenant's bar, but there was no CIB on his chest. A Colt .45 hung easily from the cartridge belt at his hip. He was chomping on the short stub of a well-chewed cigar when Chamberlin reported to him.

Chamberlin noticed he was not wearing his CIB. He felt a little embarrassed. Pierce took note of Chamberlin's CIB. He said nothing about it, but wondered.

He introduced Chamberlin to First Sergeant James Baker and then took him over to Sergeant Burfoot's mess tent where his other officers were having coffee. First Lieutenant Mike Moroney was his executive officer. First Lieutenant Jules Buckhuyht had the first platoon and First Lieutenant Jim Rau had the weapons platoon. That means I get either the second or third platoon, thought Chamberlin.

"Which platoon do you want me to have?" asked Chamberlin, anxious to know his assignment so he could get acquainted with his men.

"I don't know yet," Pierce said. "I'll think about it and let you know tomorrow.."

L Company was in a blocking position in Battalion reserve while the other two rifle companies of the battalion were on the main line of resistance. The men were living in their pup tents, since they were out of range of enemy artillery fire. All the men had rubber air mattresses to sleep on. *A lot different from World War II, when we slept on the hard, cold ground in Germany,* thought Chamberlin. Chamberlin was quartered with the

14

other officers in a large, tepee-shaped tent. The officers had cots upon which to put their air mattresses. Chamberlin condescended to the luxuries of the Korean police action by accepting an air mattress from the supply tent.

When no one was looking that first evening he took the conspicuous CIB off his fatigue jacket and stowed it away with some personal stuff. He realized now these were worn only by rear echelon men who needed them to prove their combat status. *It was a little ridiculous,* he admitted silently, *to go into combat wearing proof of having been in combat.*

But since he was now in a combat outfit which would move up to the front lines when its turn came, Chamberlin decided to prepare his equipment accordingly. From his duffle bag he brought forth twin daggers with their sharp double edges sheathed in leather scabbards. He pondered where best to carry them—on his cartridge belt, or maybe in his combat boots? He stuck them in his boots and stood up. They did not feel uncomfortable. He held them next to his cartridge belt at his hips. It was already loaded with a bayonet for his carbine, a canteen, an ammunition pouch, and a first-aid kit. There was not much room left. He decided to defer the decision for now. He was not sure what the other officers would think if they saw him with his daggers. But he did not put them back in his duffle bag. He put them in his knapsack, which he figured he would be wearing into combat when the time came. The daggers would be handy when he needed them.

The next morning Pierce remembered that he had not yet assigned Chamberlin, or even paid him much mind. In fact his thoughts were on other things, mostly the fact that he had nearly enough points to rotate back to the States. Another month and he would make it. He would escape the fate of his classmates, which he was well familiar with. He would be alive, unwounded, undecorated and probably unpromoted. A momentary feeling of ambivalence faded quickly.

He found Chamberlin stripped to his waist doing pull-ups on an improvised exercise bar in back of the officers' tent.

"Want to go up and relieve Jules on a detail?" he asked.

"Sure," agreed Chamberlin as he put his T-shirt and fatigue jacket back on.

"They're building gun positions on a secondary line of resistance. The men know what they have to do. All you'll have to do is keep 'em busy."

"Okay. Maybe I can learn something."

Because of his inferior rank, Chamberlin got into the back seat of the jeep. Pierce sat up front with the driver. They did not talk on the ride toward the front. Pierce wondered some more about his new officer. He had noticed that he had taken off his CIB. *Smart move,* he thought. *He had been fairly quiet. What he had said seemed okay. He did not seem too power-happy.* Pierce did not like power-happy officers who thought they knew it all. He had said he was married and had one kid and another one on the way. Pierce thought of his own son whom he had never seen. He closed his eyes and tried to shut out thoughts of Chamberlin and the war. He visualized again the latest pictures of James, Jr. The muscles of his square jaw relaxed as love for his beautiful wife and son filled his thoughts. Soon we will be together—the three of us. The corners of his mouth curled upward in a smile. The jeep came to a stop at the end of the road. His eyes reopened and his jaw tensed again.

"Wait here for me," Pierce told the driver.

16

Chamberlin followed Pierce up the steep trail leading to the top of the ridge. Pierce did not look back. He did not rest when he got tired. Chamberlin wondered if he was being tested. But he was in good shape, so he was not worried. He could keep up. However, soon his calves ached and his thighs felt the need for oxygen. His heart pounded and his lungs throbbed. The distance between them increased but Pierce still did not look back or stop. Chamberlin started sweating. Paths forked off from the trail they were on. There were sharp turns. He lost sight of Pierce. He wondered if he could get lost. He did not know where they were or where the enemy was. He had no map or compass, not that these would have helped. He did not even have his daggers with him.

Suddenly he had to urinate. He stopped, turned to the side of the trail and relieved himself. It felt good to rest. He took a drink from his canteen. If that is the way Pierce is, piss on him, he thought. Anger mixed with his apprehension and seemed to dilute it. After a brief respite, he continued the climb. Up ahead Pierce finally stopped and waited at a bend in the trail until Chamberlin nearly caught up to him. Then he turned without a word of sympathy or concern and led Chamberlin on to their destination.

The men were building bunkers out of logs and sandbags. Some were cutting trees in the surrounding woods, some were carrying the timbers to the place of construction, others filled sandbags with the sandy dirt dug from the trenches connecting the bunkers, while still others constructed the fortifications.

Lieutenants Pierce and Buckhuyt went back down the hill. Chamberlin stayed with the work detail. He walked among the men. He asked questions but gave no orders. The men smiled behind his back. They did not appear to be working very hard. One group faced an obstacle. A large stump, partly rotted with age, blocked the field of fire of a machine-gun emplacement. A pick, shovel, and axe remained unproductive in idle hands as the men contemplated and speculated about the difficulty of the task of removing the dead stump.

"What we need is some dynamite," opined a short, black lad. "You can get us some dynamite, Lieutenant, can't you?"

"You think I can get you some dynamite?" reflected Chamberlin. He was not sure what he could get. Nobody had told him anything yet. "Probably it would take longer to do that than it would to chop it out with an axe."

"Oh, you can't chop it out. We've been working on it all morning. It's too hard to chop."

Perhaps he was right. Chamberlin did not know. He took off his cartridge belt and placed it and his carbine neatly on the ground to the side.

"Let me see your axe," he requested.

He took the single-bitted axe in his hands, felt the edge with his thumb, spit on the palms of his hands, rubbed them together to spread the spit, and then addressed the stump. After a few well-placed chops, he stopped. Some of the men smiled, thinking he had given up. But he removed his steel helmet and fatigue jacket, placed them next to his other gear, and resumed chopping. Chips flew. In short order, the stump was reduced to a mass of chips and small pieces. The smiles of the men changed to looks of wonderment. They had never seen an officer work like this. Sergeant Hy Davidson, the platoon sergeant, was silent and kept a poker face.

Chamberlin smiled. "I used to be a lumberjack," he said in a half-apology and half-boast about his proficiency with an axe.

For the rest of the day Chamberlin chopped logs, filled sandbags, dug trenches, and helped put bunkers together. Perhaps the men in his immediate proximity worked a little harder to emulate him. He did not know. He hoped so. At least, he learned something and got some work done. When the work detail returned to the company area in late afternoon, Chamberlin smelled of sweat and dirt. He was tired. Some men of the third platoon, which had made up the work detail, hoped Chamberlin would be their new platoon leader. Sergeant Davidson did not. He did not think leaders should work.

The next day Pierce assigned Chamberlin to the second platoon.

3

In June of 1952, the Red Chinese and North Korean armies were drawn up against the United Nations forces across the mountainous middle of Korea. Two years before, the war had started at approximately the same place when the North Koreans had invaded the South. The war was stalemated now in the sense that neither side was making any sustained drives to capture large amounts of land. Peace talks were in progress at Panmunjon. These seemed stalemated too. While the peace emissaries shuffled and dealt their diplomatic cards at the conference table for political pots, the fighting forces shuffled their men and weapons and dealt death for tiny geographical pots along the 38th parallel.

Shortly after Lieutenant Chamberlin joined L Company, they were moved onto the main line of resistance. Out across a valley, rugged peaks meshed with the sky to form a jagged horizon. Directly in front of L company's positions was a long ridge extending northward perpendicular to the front lines. Another ridge cut across it to give it a T-Bone appearance. Hence it was called "T-Bone." The end of T-Bone toward L Company was called "Eerie." The Chinese held Eerie and a long trench could be seen leading along the ridge toward their main line. Off to the right front of Chamberlin's second platoon were two small knolls that stuck up prominently from the valley floor. Because of their shape they were known as "Dagmar." Their perfectly rounded appearance had made some sexually preoccupied name maker think of the busts of the current Hollywood bombshell.

As soon as they were settled in their bunkers on the MLR, Chamberlin removed his twin daggers from his knapsack. Now was the time to decide how to integrate them with his other battle equipment. He finally opted to wear them stuck in his boots, on the outside opposite the inside zippers. He had had these sewed into his boots at Fort Benning to save the trouble of lacing them every day. Leather thongs through slits in the sheaths were wrapped around his legs above the boots and tied on the inside to hold the daggers in place. He also tied down his bayonet scabbard with another leather thong around his thigh.

Lieutenant Moroney called on the field phone. "Chamberlin, send one of your squads out to the right knoll of Dagmar. Battalion wants us to occupy it and dig machine-gun emplacements there to fire on Eerie."

This is it, thought Chamberlin. He had wondered how he would feel, how he would react. Would it be like stage fright? Would it be like the fear of a boxer before he enters the ring? Would his heart pound? Would he say or do the wrong thing?

His reaction took him completely by surprise. His heart did not race. There was no lump in his throat when he spoke. In fact, he was a little angry because this was nothing like it had been in training at Fort Benning. Moroney had given him no detailed instructions.

"What's the situation?" he asked in a low, calm voice. "Are there any Chinks out there?"

"Not to our knowledge."

"Should I go out with the squad or stay here?"

"You'd better stay there. If you have any questions,

ask Sergeant Sides. He knows what to do. The main thing is to get those gun positions dug out there."

"Yes, Sir," answered Chamberlin, a little perturbed at such a sloppy order.

"Sergeant Sides, whose turn is it to go out?" Chamberlin asked his platoon sergeant.

"Sergeant Browne's," answered Sides. A hint of nervousness seemed to have infiltrated his normally calm demeanor. "What do we have to do?"

"We have to send a squad out to Dagmar. Have him report here."

The phone jangled again. It was Moroney.

"Chamberlin, have the men pick up picks and shovels at the Company CP. Have 'em ready to go in fifteen minutes. The artillery is going to lay a smoke screen for them."

"Yes, Sir," Chamberlin said to Moroney on the phone. "Never mind getting Browne," to Sides. "We haven't got time. We'll go there. Harry, bring a roll of commo wire and a phone and come with us. Amos, stay here while we're gone."

Harry Cottrell was Chamberlin's communications man and Sergeant Amos was the assistant platoon sergeant.

Chamberlin felt tall as he led Sides and Cottrell to Browne's squad area. It was happening. He was giving orders and they were being followed in a combat situation. He quickly told Browne what had to be done and then took up a position where he could watch the men move down the lonely slope into no-man's-land and along the trail to the right knoll of Dagmar.

Artillary exploded out in front of the men and a smoke screen spread lazily across the valley floor between the Chinese and Browne's squad. Chamberlin watched through field glasses as Browne led his men past the base of the left knoll toward the right knoll. One of them carried the roll of commo wire hooked to a field phone.

"Good work," commented Lieutenant Pierce who had slipped up silently next to Chamberlin. "Good timing." He patted Chamberlin on the shoulder.

"Thanks. Maybe I should've gone with them."

A puff of smoke and dust rose from the left knoll followed by the sound of a mortar round exploding.

"Those fucking Chinks aren't so dumb," said Chamberlin. "They know what's behind that smoke screen."

"Yeah," agreed Pierce. "But at least they can't see them. It's better than being wide open."

More mortar rounds hit the left knoll in a saturation pattern. Browne's squad moved swiftly onto the right knoll. As though drawn by a magnet, the mortar rounds followed them. Browne's men found refuge quickly in the bunkers, foxholes, and trenches already there, and stayed low.

A little later Browne called on the field phone. "We're getting the hell shelled out of us out here. One of my men has already been hit and we can't do anything. As soon as we start digging they start throwing shit at us. They're firing from high ground on both sides of us right down our throats. What am I supposed to do? We got to get Coplin back. He's bleeding bad."

"Okay Bob, I'll see if I can get some more smoke out there and send some men with a stretcher."

"I might as well send Charles back, too. He cracked up and I can't do anything with him."

After the stretcher detail got back, bearing the wounded Eddy Coplin and accompanied by Charles Hale, a casualty of a different sort, Chamberlin tried to

23

talk to Hale. It was useless. Hale was completely withdrawn from reality. All he wanted to do was to go home to his mother. Ironically, Chamberlin thought later, that's probably what happened. He wondered how many men cracked up for that reason. Could it also happen to him? He quickly dismissed the thought. Coplin was sent on back to the Battalion aid station with a badly wounded arm.

Toward evening a random mortar round severed the commo wire, between Chamberlin's CP and Browne's squad. Chamberlin had been ordered to have Browne's men stay on the right knoll that night to continue digging machine-gun emplacements. We must have communications, thought Chamberlin.

"Want me to locate the break?" asked Cottrell, seeming to sense Chamberlin's feelings.

"Can you?" asked Chamberlin.

"I'll try."

Chamberlin looked at Cottrell with a new respect.

"I'll get some smoke out there to cover you," he said.

He watched Cottrell as he moved out, lifting the wire hand over hand looking for the break. Smoke landed out front but there was too little of it and wind blew it away too soon. Cottrell moved slowly and diligently on as though unmindful of danger. He was all alone. Chamberlin felt compelled to follow him, to protect him. He left the trench and moved swiftly down the trail. He was nearly up to Cottrell when Cottrell found the break in the wire at the base of the left knoll. Chamberlin stopped a few yards away and knelt on the ground to lower his silhouette as Cottrell spliced the wires.

They were now closer to the right knoll of Dagmar than the friendly front line behind them. There was no more smoke. They would have been more exposed to go back than to go forward. Chamberlin signaled to Cottrell to move on out to Browne's position. He waited until Cottrell made it. A mortar round slammed into the path behind Cottrell. He debated for a few seconds whether to return to the MLR to be with his other three squads, as Moroney had advised, or to go to be with his men who were in danger. Another mortar round hit a few yards behind him. He heard the familiar whistle as it rotated and its tail fins guided it true through the air to its deadly destination. He jumped up and sprinted the hundred yards to the top of the right knoll and eased himself into a bunker occupied by Browne and several of his men. Mortars and direct-fire weapons pounded the position. It was as if the Chinese knew exactly where they were and what they were doing.

"Here, Lieutenant," said Browne. "Take my place and let me sit next to the entrance. I've got an armored vest on and you haven't."

"No, that's all right," replied Chamberlin. "Stay where you are."

Browne, Chamberlin, and most of Browne's men were crammed into a hole in the ground. Some logs had been placed over the top and sandbags and dirt topped these to make about a foot of overhead cover. They were safe here except from a direct hit or a piece of shrapnel flying through the entrance.

An attention-commanding voice sounded through the entrance. "I think I see the bastard."

Chamberlin looked out and saw Private First Class Jack Neathery lying on his belly on the crest of the hill peering through field glasses toward Eerie. His right arm was bare where his fatigue jacket sleeve had been torn off. His blond hair stood out vividly as he laid his steel helmet aside to prevent it from deflecting the magnetic needle of his compass as he took an azimuth reading. His sky-blue eyes sparkled with excitement as he shouted an azimuth and estimated range to the enemy weapon. Chamberlin watched and listened with fascination as Browne relayed the information back to the artillery observer at the Company CP. Within seconds an artillery round was on the way. It fell short and to the right.

"Up 200, left 100," shouted Neathery.

Another round landed.

"Down 100, left 50."

Chamberlin stuck his head out to watch the artillery rounds bracketed in. An enemy round exploded a few feet in front of the bunker. Chamberlin flinched. Neathery did not bat an eye.

"Up 50, right 25. Okay, let 'em have it."

A few seconds later several artillery rounds exploded in a cluster on the side of Eerie.

Neathery continued to scan the hills to the north for puffs of smoke, evidence of enemy weapons.

"Jack is the best fucking soldier I ever saw," said Browne. "He deserves a medal for what he's done today."

"Why don't you put him in for one when we get back?" asked Chamberlin.

"I will. Vincent is another one. He was out there in the open this morning giving Eddie first aid when shells were landing all around him and he didn't pay any attention to 'em. Eddie would've bled to death if it hadn't been for Tony."

Tony Vincent was the aid man assigned to the second platoon.

"Put them both in," Chamberlin said.

Soon after dusk, mortar rounds started raining in on the position.

"Those bastards know we're here," said Browne.

"They'll probably send a patrol out here tonight."

"Think we can hold 'em off?" asked Chamberlin. He thought it wise to rely on the combat experience of these men. They had been in Korea longer than he had.

"I don't know. Two casualties already today. That leaves me with six men. And with no overhead cover for the rest of my men, I won't have them long if they keep shelling us like this."

Chamberlin noted that Browne had not included him and Cottrell, but he let it ride. Pride is a poor protector.

"What do you think we should do?"

"I think we ought to get the hell out of here before they come. They're on top of you before you know it."

"Ring the Company CP for me, Harry," said Chamberlin.

Moroney answered.

"We're getting a lot of shelling, Mike," reported Chamberlin. "Sergeant Browne thinks we ought to get out of here. He thinks they'll hit this place with a patrol tonight."

"You can't pull out. Battalion says we've got to get some gun positions dug out there." Moroney sounded nervous.

"Well, we aren't going to dig any damn positions while they're throwing shit at us or while we're listening for a patrol. We can't defend the damn place and dig too."

Chamberlin's sudden show of rebellious spunk surprised Moroney. "Well, you want to talk to Battalion?" he asked.

"I don't give a shit who I talk to. I'll talk to the fucking general if you want me to. There isn't any damn sense in my men getting killed out here for nothing."

"Okay, I'll hook you up to Battalion."

Major Moore, the Batallion operations officer, answered. Chamberlin told him essentially the same thing he had told Moroney. This was more than Moore could handle. He put Colonel Spottswood on the phone.

"What's the trouble, Chamberlin?" Spottswood asked.

"We're getting the hell shelled out of us and want to get the hell out of here."

"Listen, Chamberlin, I can't tell you why, but we've got to have those positions dug out there."

"Well, dead men can't dig. What the hell are we, a suicide squad? I didn't know American forces used those kind of tactics."

A short, heavy silence ensued. Spottswood remembered Chamberlin well and how he had felt about him. Somehow it now seemed less important to do exactly as Colonel Sandlin had ordered.

Finally Spottswood spoke. "Chamberlin, can you pull back to the knoll behind you until the shelling lets up, and then go back to work on the positions?"

"We can try, Sir. That's better than getting killed here now."

Browne and his men had listened to Chamberlin's conversation with keen interest. They were surprised and glad that they finally had a platoon leader that would speak up for them. However, logic would have told them that this courage to speak up for them was not the kind of courage that wins battles or medals for gallantry. Quite the contrary, the fear of death gave him the guts to confront a lesser danger, the mere wrath of his superiors. It did not compare with the courage of Neathery and Vincent.

"Who knows how to get back to the left knoll?"

asked Chamberlin. It was pitch dark and he did not trust his own sense of direction or geographical orientation.

"I do," volunteered Neathery. "I was out here before with the First Cavalry."

"Okay, you lead. Browne, have your men follow Jack. I'll bring up the rear."

Jack Neathery, Bob Browne, Frenchy Bowman, Elroy Olsen, George Chalifour, Bill West, Harry Cottrell, and Al Chamberlin wormed their way slowly westward toward the left knoll. In the dark the footing was precarious at best. To make it worse a light drizzle turned the sandy dirt into slippery goo. But somehow they made it. They found cover in another bunker large enough to hold them all. Chamberlin had no idea how large it was. He could not see anything. They communicated by touch and low whispers. No one dared to strike a match or light a cigarette.

It went unspoken, but there was no intent to return to the right knoll that night. Even Colonel Spottswood probably knew that.

Moroney called and said there had been a change in plans. They did not have to go back to the right knoll.

In the damp darkness of the bunker, Chamberlin settled down and leaned his back against the sandbagged wall. A hand feeling for a place to sit or lie felt his leg. He spread his legs gently so as not to kick anyone.

"There's room here in front of me," he said.

A warm, smelly body settled down in front of him. Gradually it leaned back against his chest, like a child settling in the lap of his mother. Chamberlin welcomed the warmth.

"What's your name?" he asked softly.

"Bowman. Mason Bowman," answered the body with a soft southern drawl.

"Try to get some rest, Mason," whispered Chamberlin, as his arms encircled the body in front of him, partly because there was no other place to put them comfortably, and partly because it seemed a natural thing to do, to hold one of his men close to him. He tried to put the name with a face. He thought Bowman was the little, short, dark-haired fellow from New Orleans, the one that carried a BAR which was nearly as long as he was tall. The men called him "Frenchy."

4

When General Ruffner took over the 45th Division in late May, 1952, he decided to move the outpost line of resistance a little further north of the main line of resistance to take away from the Chinese forces some key observation vantage points. According to historical accounts, there were about a dozen of these Chinese outposts strung out along the front of the 180th, 179th, and the 279th Infantry Regiments which made up the 45th Division. Operation "Counter" was designed to take these outposts away from the Chinese and perhaps earn General Ruffner another star.

As of the morning of June 14, some phases of operation "Counter" had already been accomplished. Another outpost was scheduled to be taken that day—Eerie, Hill 183 on General Ruffner's war map. That was why Browne's squad had been sent to dig the gun positions on Dagmar, so they could be used to support the assault on Eerie."

After Lieutenant Chamberlin, Private First Class Cottrell, Sergeant Browne, and his squad returned to the MLR in the early light of dawn, they had a few moments to rest and look after their gear.

Chamberlin discovered that he had lost one of his daggers. Also the zippers on his boots had given out, rendering them useless as footgear. Fortunately the supply sergeant happened to have a pair that fit him. They were not as fancy as the zippered ones. They had split-leather shoe parts with the two-buckled top parts—the kind you could not shine. He also found that his remaining dagger fit neatly into a trench knife (carbine bayonet) scabbard. He got another scabbard from supply, put it on his cartridge belt symmetrically opposite the one on his right hip and tied it down to his left thigh. Now he looked like a two-bayonet man.

Soon after morning chow, feverish activity broke out in the 179th and 180th Infantry areas. Companies E, F, and G of the 180th were moved into positions for the initial assault. Companies I, K, and L of the 179th were alerted to be ready to move out to reinforce or relieve the attacking companies as needed.

Mortars and 87-mm recoilless rifles along the MLR opened up on Eerie. Heavier artillery from farther back pounded Eerie and the trenches behind it. The shelling continued throughout the day, increasing in intensity as H-hour, the time the foot soldiers would move out into the attack, neared. Low-flying, speedy jets swooped in and delivered their rockets and bombs. A solitary spotter plane hovered high above the target to show the death-dealing boys where to drop their hardware. Slower flying, propeller-driven planes of World War II vintage ripped paths of dust across Eerie with their .50-caliber machine-guns and 20-mm cannons. In the afternoon, the flyboys made it even hotter by dropping flaming blankets of napalm on the occupants of the trenches and foxholes of Eerie.

Big shots—Majors, Colonels, and Generals, along with their aides—wandered around on the MLR. Most of them had large, expensive-looking cameras and binoculars. They appeared to be looking for the best vantage points to view the action out front and take pictures.

32

They are like little boys playing with tin soldiers, thought Chamberlin. They will show those pictures to their friends back home and brag about the action they were in.

A half-track with quad-fifties rattled up to a position near where Chamberlin was watching. The gunner fired a few bursts at Eerie. Chamberlin saw a group of Chinese coming down the long trench toward Eerie from the higher ground to the north. It was a perfect target for machine-guns. He picked up the phone on the back of the half-track and gave a firing order to the gunner. Machine-gun bullets raised a cloud of dust in an elliptical pattern where the Chinese had been.

Did we get them? wondered Chamberlin. If so, it was perhaps the first time he had ever been directly involved in killing enemy soldiers. In World War II his outfit had always been moving. Seldom had they set up their machine-guns to fire on the Germans. And when they had, it had always been indirect fire. In that type of fire you could not see your target. He had no particular feeling about whether the Chinese had been killed or not.

E Company moved out across the valley floor at 1600 hours. Despite the massive shelling and napalm burning, the Chinese welcomed them with withering fire and rose from their holes on Eerie to engage them in hand-to-hand struggle for possession of the hill. Chamberlin wondered how they could have lived through such a shelling. They must be really dug in, he thought.

Lieutenant Moroney called on the phone. "Al, get your men ready to move out. E Company's running into a lot of trouble out there. We may have to reinforce them."

"What should the men take with them?"

"One K ration and all the ammo they can carry. I'm

sending a supply of K rations over to your CP now. Don't move until I give the word." Moroney hung up.

Questions popped into Chamberlin's mind. Which way would they go? Straight out across the valley floor in front of them, or follow E Company's route back around the hill to the left? What would the men do with the rest of their stuff? Should he call a meeting?

"Jim," Chamberlin addressed his platoon sergeant. "We may have to move out."

"Move out!" cried Sergeant Sides in immediate panic. "How can we move out? The men haven't got their gear ready. Where are we going?"

Side's nervousness had a strange effect on Chamberlin. It made him both angry and calm.

"Don't get your piss hot, Jim," he said slowly. "Harry, get the squad leaders on the phone for a conference call."

The squad leaders reported on the phone; "Crimins, first squad; Browne, second squad; McAfee, third squad; Jackson, weapons squad."

"Men, we may have to move out. Have your men pack their gear and stand by. K rations are on the way. Send one man from each squad to my CP to pick them up. One K ration and all the ammo they can carry per man. Have the men pack the rest of their stuff separately. Be sure they have water and give them some salt tablets. It's hotter than hell out there. Stay by the phone for further orders."

The men got ready to go.

Chamberlin told Sides to stay by the phone and went outside the bunker to watch with field glasses E Company's progress up Eerie.

Men rushed up the slopes a few feet and hit the dirt. Others leapfrogged them. Some turned and ran back.

34

Were they bugging out? wondered Chamberlin. He hated that expression. Everybody used it. Through the glasses he saw a man's helmet and part of his head fly through the air. The body beneath sank to the ground and rolled down the slope a few feet. It stopped and stayed still. Poor bastard, thought Chamberlin.

Moroney called again. "Al, we may not have to move out tonight. Just stay ready. Have the men get their extra stuff ready to turn into supply."

"Okay, Mike."

Chamberlin told his men to get all the rest they could and stay ready.

Corporal Garrett, the mail clerk, brought mail. Chamberlin got a letter from Ruby, a woman he had been seeing when he was stationed at Benning. She wrote the usual sweet stuff and signed with all her love. He stuck her letter in his breast pocket, giving no thought to the possibility that it might get back to his wife in case he did not. No mail from his wife. He had received a short note from her on 12 June that she had given birth to a healthy boy on 24 May. His elation had been somewhat embittered by her delay in telling him. She had not even bothered to use an airmail stamp. Stingy bitch. Everybody else got a telegram when they became fathers. She was probably still mad because he had not tried to get an extension of his leave before shipping overseas, so he could be with her when she had the baby. To him, that would have been the chicken thing to do. Maybe he had been remiss in his familial duties, but he would be damned before he would let anyone think of him as "chicken."

Besides, he had never quite gotten over the sendoff she had given him when he left for active duty on 3 July 1951. A friend had handed him a summons to appear in court on nonsupport charges. It was not that he had not been supporting her. They had been living on the money he had been getting from the GI Bill while he had been in college. Plus he had been working at G.E. It was the fact that she did not think he was going to send her any money while he was in the Army. *That was real faith*, he thought bitterly. Communications between them had broken down completely. He had ignored the summons, sent her an allotment, and she had come down to be with him for a couple of months while he was at Fort Dix. That was when she had gotten pregnant with the baby, Ronald. But it had not been the same; it probably never would be. Love had to be based on trust.

He glanced at his right palm. It was always comforting to look at the long lifeline extending down toward his wrist. He always remembered the words of "Old Lady" Cushion, an eccentric old woman who had lived in his home town back in Underhill, Vermont. She had wanted to look at his palm when he was home on furlough just before he had shipped over to Europe in World War II. She had told him that he had nothing to worry about. Nothing was going to happen to him in the war. He wondered if her fortune-telling and his own lifeline, took into account this war. He felt reassured that it did.

The next morning they moved out—not forward, but back to the Company headquarters area. They had a hot breakfast. They turned in their extra gear and waited. Rumors flew. They heard that E and F Companies had accomplished their missions but had sustained heavy casualties. Nobody seemed to know for sure. They had another hot meal at noon. Then they were loaded onto trucks and taken along dusty roads. They unloaded at an assembly point in back of a hill that screened them from Eerie.

Lieutenant Pierce held a meeting of his platoon leaders. Lieutenant Rau was not longer with them. He had rotated just in time. Pierce introduced his replacement, Lieutenant George Price, a tall, well-built black man.

"We have to relieve E Company," he said bluntly. "We'll move out in this order: First Platoon, Weapons Platoon, Second Platoon and Third Platoon. Jules, your platoon will occupy the trench around the top of the hill and be responsible for a perimeter defense from 10 o'clock to 2 o'clock." Pierce drew a circle on the ground with a stick to symbolize the face of a clock. "The weapons platoon will be attached to you and set up in your area. My CP will be with the First Platoon. Al, move your platoon on to the right side of Eerie. Your zone of the perimeter will be from 2 o'clock to 6 o'clock. George, your platoon will be responsible for the left side of Eerie from 6 o'clock to 10 o'clock. We move out at 1400 hours. I will be with the First Platoon. Mike, you better lead the Weapons Platoon and I'll see you on Eerie."

Chamberlin relayed the orders to his squad leaders and gave each his specific order of march and assignment.

L Company moved out across the valley toward Eerie. Incoming Russian-made hardware slowed their advance. Chamberlin's men rested behind the hill. Chamberlin stood off to the side a little so he could keep his eyes on them and watch for the signal to move up. This was the last sanctuary. Around the curve in the road up ahead, the hill would no longer hide them from the enemy's view or shield them from flying shrapnel. He looked at his men. Some were seasoned combat veterans; some were raw replacements. They were all scared, except maybe Jack Neathery and Melnie Dawes. Dawes was an Indian boy from Kansas. Chamberlin had heard that everybody was scared in combat. He was not sure that was true, but he knew he was scared. His greatest fear was that he would screw up and that some of his men would get killed as a result.

Up ahead a jeep swung around the bend. A Catholic chaplain got out and asked the men if any of them would like to have him say a Mass for them. Many of the men were eager for this since they might die soon. Perhaps this was like the last rites. Chamberlin did not know. The short, slightly fat chaplain went through an elaborate ceremony.

Unfortunately, the site picked for the ritual was in the narrow road, and no vehicle could pass while the chaplain held forth. This would have been no concern to Chamberlin had not a convoy of several more jeeps suddenly appeared around the bend in the road coming from the battle area up front. These jeeps were loaded with stretchers bearing wounded men.

The jeeps stopped, the rear ones barely out of the danger zone up ahead. Chamberlin looked at the men kneeling in prayer. They were all healthy and whole. Surely, he thought, they would give way for the wounded and dying. But they did not move. He looked at the priest as he mumbled his Latin mumbo-jumbo and waved his hand in the sign of the cross. Surely he would stop, or at least interrupt, this foolishness to let men in real need pass on toward the medical station in the rear. But no, he did not stop. He continued for what seemed an eternity. Should he, only a second lieutenant, ask the chaplain, who was a captain, to let the jeeps pass?

Suddenly Chamberlin had to urinate. He wondered if it would be sacrilegious to piss while men prayed. *No worse than holding a prayer meeting in the way of dying comrades*, he though satirically. He turned his back on the men along the road and moved far enough away for pseudo-privacy. He did what he had to do.

The signal to move up was passed back from up around the bend. The priest hurriedly finished his crosses and returned to his jeep. The kneeling men rose. All the men gathered themselves together. Chamberlin stepped back toward his men.

"Okay men, let's go," he said softly.

They followed Private Dawes, the point man, on around the bend in the road.

5

Mortar rounds buzzed as they landed among the men. Artillery whistled in. Those you hear won't hurt you, veterans said. The men hit the dirt. Chamberlin lay there a moment. He got to his knees to survey the situation. It was less than half a mile to the foot of Eerie and escape from the view of the enemy. They would be dead if they stayed out here in the open long, he calculated.

"Come on," he hollered. "Let's go. Move out. On your fucking feet."

He moved quickly among the men, nudging them to their feet with his boots and rifle butt. Up and down the column he went to be sure that everybody got going.

"Stay low and move out as fast as you can," he ordered loudly.

All of the men wore armored vests. They also were weighed down heavily with ammo and weapons. Chamberlin had decided against an armored vest for the sake of mobility and speed. When he had to move fast, he wanted to be able to. He was glad now that he was not encumbered by extra weight. He would take his chances on getting hit.

Funny, he thought. He had been scared as hell when the first rounds had hit near him. But then, when he had seen his men prostrated and immobilized by fear, something snapped in him. His mind seemed to function more clearly and logically. His own fear spurred him to action as the welfare of his men became uppermost in his mind. His strength and agility increased. He would never have kicked a man the size of Browne in the ass under normal circumstances. Browne was a big man, probably four inches taller and fifty pounds heavier than Chamberlin. And he looked and acted tough. Chamberlin knew from their experience on Dagmar that Browne was a good combat man with plenty of guts. But even men of courage hit the ground instinctively when they are being shelled to make themselves as small a target as possible. Chamberlin's increased perception seemed to tell him to get his key men going so the rest would follow. He had recognized Browne as one of his key men.

The men responded to Chamberlin's orders and courage, and soon the second platoon followed Dawes up the rear slope of Eerie and on around to the right side of the shell-pocked hill.

"Dig in as soon as you get into position," Chamberlin had ordered.

Chamberlin picked a spot for his CP in back of the second squad and toward the top of the hill. He told Cottrell to string commo wire to each squad while he moved around the entire platoon front to see that every man was all right and in a good position. Surprisingly, all his men had survived the barrage in the open valley uninjured.

Chamberlin checked to see that the First Squad had made contact with the First Platoon on the left. He went to the right flank of his platoon and then on around the rear slope of Eerie looking for the left flank of Lieutenant Price's Third Platoon with which he was supposed to connect.

Suddenly he saw a dead Chinese soldier lying face down in the dirt. At least he thought he was dead. He did not move. He was bareheaded. Probably an officer, because he had long hair. Chamberlin reached down and touched him. He looked around the battlefield. He was all alone with the dead man. It was an eerie feeling. Suddenly it became very important to him to get back to his men and get dug in before dark. To hell with establishing contact with the Third Platoon. He could not do everything. The Chinks probably would not come up the rear slope of Eerie anyhow.

When he got back to his CP he called Moroney and told him about the dead Chink and that he had not been able to make contact with the Third Platoon. Moroney told him not to worry about it. The Third Platoon probably had not got out there yet.

Chamberlin was a little upset with himself about how he had reacted to the dead Chink. Why had he not searched the body for papers, maps, and stuff? Why had he been so apprehensive?

He went over to check with Sergeants Sides and Amos to see how they were doing. They were well dug in and had plenty of ammunition, including a whole crate of grenades.

He noted that Sides seemed to be functioning okay now. After that fit of nervousness the day before, he had been quiet and did what he was told.

Cottrell had strung wire to each squad and to the Company CP while Chamberlin had been inspecting the platoon front. Now they worked together digging a two-man foxhole for themselves. By dark they were dug in deep enough so that their heads were below ground level when they sat in the hole. They stopped for a moment's respite.

"You did a good job getting the phones hooked up, Harry. You're a good man."

"Thank you, Sir."

"Let's have a bite to eat."

They munched on their one K ration, assuming someone would bring them more food the next day or that they would not have to stay out there too long.

Darkness, loneliness, and silence settled over the battlefield. Men huddled close together in their two- or three-man foxholes. They were glad they were not alone. The few feet of void between foxholes became a mysterious menace. Many enemy could be there. They kept their eyes peeled for movement and ears open for sounds of danger. The darkness protected and scared them at the same time.

Suddenly all hell broke loose. Enemy hardware started pouring in. Mortars, artillery, small-arms fire—the works. The earth shook. Dirt, shrapnel, and debris filled the air and pelted the men and weapons in the foxholes as it returned to rest. It clogged the weapons and buried ammunition. It drove fear into the hearts of the brave and the cowardly, the strong and the weak, the big and the small. It did not discriminate. It tore into dirt, metal, and flesh. It made and filled holes. Some men huddled under their steel helmets and prayed helplessly to an unknown God that they would not be hit. The thinking men tried to protect the working mechanism of their weapons by covering them with their bodies to keep the dirt out. They fumbled in the dark for hand grenades and ammo to keep them ready for use.

I hope that is the last one, Chamberlin thought after each close one. He did not pray to any God. He was agnostic. He would have hated any God who allowed man to treat his brother so brutally.

This was not ordinary shelling. Thousands of rounds slammed into Eerie. Out on the cross of T-Bone, I

Company was undergoing a similar pounding. It could mean only one thing. The Chinese intended to take back their lost real estate. Chamberlin hoped his men were alert enough to see the enemy before it was too late to defend themselves. He almost hoped for the assault of enemy foot soldiers, for then he knew the artillery would at least slacken or move its strike zone.

Chamberlin felt for Cottrell. "You all right?"

Cottrell welcomed the touch. "I'm okay," he whispered.

Suddenly Cottrell started leaving the foxhole.

"Where are you going?" asked Chamberlin.

"I have to urinate."

"Well, don't go outside while they're shelling us. Piss in the foxhole."

"I can't go in our foxhole. That's not right."

"Fuck false modesty." Chamberlin fumbled around in the dark and found an empty ration can. "Here. Piss in this can and dump it over the top. Then give me the can. I have to piss, too."

Sharing the pee can did not breed contempt, as they had been taught it would in ROTC classes. Rather, it augmented the bond of respect and friendship between them.

The shelling let up a little. Some men from the top of the hill ran down through Chamberlin's platoon area. A few of his men appeared to join them. Chamberlin thought they were bugging out. Was one of his worse fears coming true?

A loud, excited voice shouted from the First Platoon area. "They're coming through up here! Al, bring your men up here!"

Chamberlin thought he recognized the voice as that of Moroney, but he ignored it. He did not give a shit who it was. He was not about to have his men make targets of themselves by running around in the open.

Chamberlin stood tall in his foxhole. "Stay where you are, men," he ordered. "Stay in your holes. Fight from your foxholes. You have the advantage when you're in your holes. You can see the enemy but he can't see you."

By now friendly artillery had filled the air with flares. They parachuted to the ground, lighting the darkness around them on their leisurely descent. Outside the company perimeter the enemy was betrayed by the light. Their mantle of invisibility was removed.

Sergeant Bill West and Private First Class Calvin Knox rose from their foxholes when they saw the men from the other platoon bugging out through their area.

"Where the fuck you think you're going?" shouted Knox. "You stupid bastards, you're running right into their artillery. Get your fucking asses back up the hill and into your fucking holes."

West and Knox herded the crazed men back up the slopes and into their positions.

But while their positions were undefended some Chinese troops had broken through the First Platoon perimeter. From the top of the hill above Sergeant Crimin's first squad, they lobbed their "potato-masher" grenades at the First Squad's foxholes.

R.A. Boyd turned his BAR on them and mowed down a few.

Melnie Dawes picked off more of them with his M1 before a grenade landed in his foxhole. It wounded him severely below the waist. He could no longer move his legs.

Crimins managed to get off one shot from his M1 before it jammed. Other grenades landed in his foxhole. He thought there were three. He instinctively grabbed one to throw it out of the hole. Too late. There were too many. The explosions ripped the ring finger and the little finger off his left hand. Shrapnel tore into his arms, shoulders and face. He could not see. The pain was excruciating. He screamed for help. Blood, dirt, flesh, gunpowder, and shrapnel mingled on his mangled face. He held it in his bloody hands and continued to cry for help. Others heard his screams but were too busy at their own positions to go to his assistance immediately.

Finally the Chinese were repulsed from the First Platoon area. After what seemed like an eternity of pain to Crimins, he and Dawes were evacuated from their foxholes to the company aid station in the trench on top of the hill. As they lay there, Crimins moaning in agony. Dawes in silent paralysis, a mortar hit Dawes dead center. Dawes was dead.

Neathery spotted Chinese soldiers crawling up the slopes toward the second platoon. "They're coming this way!" he yelled. "Holler at the yellow bastards, men. Swear at 'em. Holler 'dunee.' That means fuck you in Chinese. It scares the hell out of 'em."

Big Bob Browne rose to his full height and bellowed, "You dirty, little yellow bastards, come and get us. I'll cut your goddamn heart out with my bayonet. Come on up and tangle assholes with some real men. Dunee, dunee!"

Browne fired his M1 rifle at the approaching enemy soldiers whenever they were definite targets. At less distinct targets he hurled grenades. He found that grenades were effective when the Chinese got real close, too. A bullet from his M1 would get only one. A grenade could take out a whole bunch of the little bastards. The problem was that he did not have very many grenades, and not much rifle ammo left either, for that matter. But he had his bayonet. None of them were going to get through his squad area as long as he was alive. And now that the artillery had lifted, he had no thought of dying.

Others joined in the chorus of swearing and cursing. Words stimulated them to action, translated their fear to bravery. The cursing and courage spread like wildfire through the platoon.

Chamberlin took up the chant. "Give 'em hell, men. The fucking little bastards. Show 'em how we can fight."

Many of the weapons had been knocked out of action by the shelling. Both machine-guns were not functioning. But a few weapons worked. These and hand grenades kept the enemy at bay. Bayonets were ready if any Chinese were able to get close enough. The guts to use them were plentiful, now that the men were inspired. Grenades were the best. They always went off. Dirt could not hurt them.

Corporal Cecil Jackson, a boy from Kansas, worked diligently trying to get the machine-guns to fire. But it was no use. They were just too damn dirty. His second gunner, Private Walter Johnson, covered him while he worked.

R.A. Boyd felt something hot hit him in the rear when the Chinese were grenading the first squad, but he stayed on his BAR. The shrapnel wound did not hurt much until later when he had time to think about it.

Telephone communications between Chamberlin's CP and the Company CP and all his squads remained miraculously intact all night. On the phone Chamberlin heard Lieutenant Buckhuyt say, "I've been hit bad. I need help." There was not much energy in his voice. His leg had been blown off and he was bleeding to death.

Later, Moroney reported that Lieutenant Pierce had gone to Buckhuyt's aid and was now missing. The Chinese had been blasting a hole through that area with recoilless rifles. Probably Pierce was blown to bits beyond recognition. He was never found. Now there was only one man left from the class of 1950 of West Point.

"We're running out of ammunition and grenades and the slant-eyed bastards are still coming," reported Sergeant Richard Webster from the first squad.

Chamberlin had quite a large supply of grenades at his CP as did Sergeants Sides and Amos at their foxhole, which was only a few yards from his. He ordered Amos to take some grenades to Webster's beleaguered squad, which was about fifty yards from his CP. Amos grabbed a box of grenades and started scrambling back toward the trench around the top of the hill. This was almost the opposite direction from Webster's squad. When it was too late to stop him, Chamberlin realized that Amos was carrying out his order, but was taking the least exposed and least dangerous route. But it was a long way around through the first platoon trenches. *He will never get there in time*, thought Chamberlin. *Stupid bastard!*

Chamberlin loaded his pockets and hands with grenades and dashed across the open area in a beeline for the first squad. He was oblivious to the burp-gun and the machine-gun fire that sprayed the area. The Chinks were closing in. Chamberlin was silhouetted against the skyline. He handed his supply of grenades gently to the men in the foxholes.

"Up here," shouted Amos who had finally reached the trench area directly above and in back of the first squad. "There are more grenades up here."

Chamberlin realized that Amos was not about to expose himself to danger by bringing the grenades down to where they were needed. The adrenaline in his system seemed to tell him what to do.

"Throw 'em down one at a time—I'll catch 'em," he shouted.

In double-play fashion Chamberlin fielded the grenades errorlessly from Amos and relayed them on to the men in the foxholes.

Later, Chamberlin stood in a foxhole with a boy from the first platoon. A BAR lay idle. Chamberlin picked it up and fired at the backflash of an enemy recoilless rifle. He burned his hand on the hot barrel by holding it like he would an M1. The lad explained to him how to fire the BAR. They worked as a team for a while. The private loaded clips while the lieutenant fired at the enemy.

Chamberlin asked the lad, "Are you scared?"

"I was while I was alone. But I'm not now with you here."

"You're doing a good job. You'll be all right. I think we've got 'em licked now." Chamberlin put his arm around the boy's shoulders. He knew that great encouragement can be transmitted by a tender touch.

Chamberlin had a lad from his platoon move into the foxhole with the lad from the First Platoon so he would not be alone.

Chamberlin found Corporal Jackson trying to fix a machine gun. He knew a lot about machine-guns from his World War II training and experience. He tried to help by adjusting the headspace, the distance between the rear of the barrel and the face of the bolt at the time of firing. He knew how to do it by tightening the barrel all the way and then backing off a couple clicks. But they could not get the gun to work. Jackson continued to work on the machine-gun. His loyal assistant, Private First Class Walter Johnson, stayed at his side and helped him as much as he could. Chamberlin gave them words of encouragement and patted them on their backs.

The incoming fire gradually subsided as the Chinese found they could not dislodge L Company from Eerie.

When L Company had moved out to Eerie on that Sunday afternoon of 15 June 1952, First Sergeant Jim Baker remained behind, but not for long. Soon after the Third Platoon had cleared the dangerous valley floor and were on the back slopes of Eerie, he led a contingent of Korean chogie boys toting five-gallon cans of water, boxes of rations, and ammunition on backpacks out to his comrades on Eerie. The thirsty, hungry men welcomed them warmly. Baker supervised the distribution of supplies and then led his Korean boys back, carrying wounded and dead.

After the battle was over Chamberlin walked among the platoon foxholes to see how his men were faring. The men watched him come and go. His silhouette was stamped on their memory. Twin daggers at his hips tied down by leather thongs around his thighs no longer seemed silly. The thongs held the scabbards down so that he could pull the daggers out quickly if need be. They held his fatigue pants tight to his thighs, thus augmenting his slimness. But now they had another function. They were the identification of the man, his insignia, his badge. He talked gently to the men as he went.

6

The reports filtered in. I Company had been overrun. Their company commander had called artillery in on their own positions. Communications with them had been lost. It was now unknown who occupied the cross of T-Bone.

The first platoon of L Company had suffered heavy casualties. Lieutenant Buckhuyt was dead. Lieutenant Pierce was missing. It was estimated that the Chinese had mounted a battalion-sized attack against Eerie. They figured that about 150 men had assaulted the right side of the hill where the Second Platoon had held forth. A larger number had attacked the First Platoon. Some of the enemy had broken through the First Platoon defenses but were later repulsed. L Company had two officers left: Moroney and Chamberlin. Lieutenant Price had been wounded and evacuated, after having demonstrated a rifle arm in throwing grenades. Word had it that he used observers to spot targets and he would hurl the deadly pineapples like a pro quarterback throws a forward pass. In fact, it was also said that he had played college football and had been destined for a pro career.

Chamberlin sat in his foxhole with Cottrell. He had told his men to clean their weapons as best they could, keep someone alert in each position, and rest as much as possible. He thought of the night and his men. He thought of Neathery igniting the men to action. He thought of Amos being afraid to expose himself to danger. At least he had helped by getting the grenades as far as he did. Sides had done nothing at all. As far as Chamberlin knew he had never left his foxhole or fired a shot. Dawes had been a damn good soldier. He wondered about Sides. All the rest of the men had done their job bravely. Sides had seemed like a cool, tough Texan when there was no danger—like the Marlboro man in the cigarette ads. Chamberlin dozed a little.

After the Chinese had given up their futile effort to retake Eerie, Sergeant Browne rested a few moments. But not for long. Worry for his brother Bill forced him to keep going. Only by action could he prevent the worry from overwhelming him. So he went from foxhole to foxhole, from man to man, in his squad area to check on his men. It was as if by looking after his men he was also looking after his brother.

Sergeant Bill Browne was a squad leader in L Company's First Platoon. He worried about Bob, too. He had led the stretcher crew that had gone to the rescue of Bob's wounded on Uncle a couple days ago. And, of course, he had checked on his brother in so doing. Now he would have liked to have been able to check on him again. But, by a quirk of fate, his squad was the only one of L Company that did not stay on Eerie that night. When they had got out there, it was decided that it was too crowded, so his squad was sent back to a reserve position for the night. At daybreak they returned to Eerie. So all night he had watched and listened as the battle raged on Eerie, knowing that his brother was in dire danger.

Bob, however, did not know that Bill was not on Eerie. As far as he knew Bill was in the trenches around the top of the hill where the Chinks had broken through.

Each man waiting for news of his brother only increased the hell and horror of war for both Bob and Bill. So Bob busied himself taking care of his men and getting them ready for whatever was to come next. He could not rest. They had made an agreement, when Bill had finally caught up with Bob by being assigned to Bob's company about the first of June, that they would not let their kinship interfere with their duties. But they both kept their eyes and ears open for word or sight of their brother.

In Chamberlin's foxhole the phone rang. He jerked alert. He reached quickly for Cottrell.

"You all right, Harry?"

"I'm all right, Sir. It was just the phone ringing."

Moroney asked on the phone, "Al, how's your platoon?"

Chamberlin replied wearily, "Oh, not too bad, I guess. We don't have much ammunition left and some of our weapons don't work. Sergeant Crimins and his squad were pretty badly shot up. There's not much left of that squad. The men are tired and hungry, but other than that we're okay."

"I Company was overrun last night. We've got to go out and retake the positions. You're the only platoon leader left. Jim, Jules, and George all got it last night. How soon can your men be ready to go?"

Chamberlin wondered if the Second Platoon would have to go alone. He wondered about the Third Platoon. Why didn't they go? A platoon sergeant could lead just as well as an officer. Maybe better. It should be their turn and they had been least hit.

But in a low, calm voice he answered slowly, "My men are always ready to go."

"Okay. Assemble them fifty yards south of my CP in fifteen minutes.

"Okay, Mike."

It was now dawn—0500 hours.

Chamberlin called each squad. He decided that Browne's squad was most ready to go. They assembled in the order they would move out; Second, Third, Weapons, and what was left of the First Squad.

"Leave the machine-guns here and move out," ordered Moroney. "When you get into the trenches, just keep going. We'll follow you as quick as we can."

Just like I figured, thought Chamberlin. *We have to do the dirty work again.* But he did not argue.

Sergeant Browne loomed above Chamberlin. "How come my squad gets all the shit? It's not our turn to lead."

Browne was a big man with a sad face. He stood a good six foot five and weighed well over 200. Even when he smiled, he looked mean. When he scowled it made smaller men shiver. His left arm was shorter than his right because of a break that had not healed properly. It hung somewhat bent. He could not straighten it all the way. Big lop-ears accentuated his meanness. Today he was in an ugly mood.

Chamberlin looked up at Browne and spoke softly. "Bob, your squad will be ahead of the other squads because you're in the best shape. But you will be behind me."

Browne alone could hear Chamberlin's words. His reply was for Chamberlin's ears only, also. "Sorry, Sir." He did not have to be told that platoon leaders did not usually act as point man in an assault. He lowered his eyes, turned, and went back to his men.

"Sides, take a position at the front of the weapons squad," ordered Chamberlin. "And be ready to take over if anything happens to me. Amos, you bring up the rear."

"Lieutenant," cried Sides in instant panic. "I can't go out there! My rifle is jammed."

54

"Fix your fucking bayonet and take your position," snapped Chamberlin.

Chamberlin moved up to the side of Browne again. In a low voice he asked, "How do you think we should do this, Bob?"

Browne was surprised at Chamberlin's humble query. He was beginning to think he was as cocky as he was bold.

Browne remembered his training well. He knew that machine-gun fire could rip hell out of a column of men, because of the elliptical strike pattern of the bullets—whereas a skirmish line was less vulnerable because it made a wider target.

"I think we ought to move out in a skirmish line," he said.

"Okay. When we get to the bottom of the hill, we'll form a skirmish line to the left," Chamberlin told Browne. He did not have to tell the rest of his men. He would use a hand signal when the time came.

He gave the signal to move out in single file. He looked at Browne. They understood each other now. "Follow me, Bob."

With long, resolute strides Chamberlin moved down the forward slope of Eerie and across the valley floor toward the cross of T-Bone.

As they were about to form a skirmish line at the base of the slope leading up to the cross of T-Bone, an order was relayed from the rear to hold up. He turned and saw Moroney leading the rest of the company behind his platoon. Moroney signaled for the company to form a skirmish line and move up the hill. Chamberlin stayed still as the men moved to his left flank, like the spokes of a giant wheel rotating around its hub.

The Browne brothers saw each other in the long skirmish line. They stood tall among the others. They waved and were relieved.

When they were parallel to the cross of the T-Bone, they all advanced up the hill in a long rank. Chamberlin's end of the line hooked as he moved more rapidly than the others. Browne and Neathery followed close behind as Chamberlin leaped into the trench with his bayonet-tipped carbine held at high port.

There were no enemy soldiers in sight. Remnants of a mutilated I Company were scattered along the trench bottom. A few were whole; many were wounded; most were dead.

Chamberlin hesitated only a moment. Moroney had said to go as far as he could. He could have turned to the right in the trench and moved south toward friendly forces. He turned left and went up the trench toward the enemy. His men followed him unhesitatingly. They passed several cave-like holes leading off from the main trench. He wondered if Chinese soldiers could come out of the holes and cut them off. He stopped.

"Maybe this is far enough," he said to Browne and Neathery as they came up to him.

"I think we ought to go back a little," said Neathery. "There are Chinks in those holes. I heard 'em talking when we went by."

"We may have to blast the bastards out with grenades," said Browne.

Chamberlin thought about prisoners. What the hell would they do with them if they captured them? They had no water or food left even for themselves. They were tired and needed rest. Somebody would have to guard them. How would they get them to come out of their holes? It seemed simpler to blast them out.

"Okay, boys, blast 'em out," he ordered.

They withdrew a few yards back down the trench. After trying to coax them out in vain, Browne and Neathery tossed grenades into each hole they passed. The Chinese occupants could be heard crying, moaning, and screaming. But none of them came out. Browne and Neathery smiled with vengeful pleasure at the muffled explosions. Chamberlin was quiet. "War brings out the beast as well as the best in man," he thought he had read somewhere.

The men huddled in the trenches and waited. Word came that they would be relieved sometime during the day. No one knew when.

Chamberlin looked out over the ridge forming the cross of the T-Bone. In a shell hole maybe fifty yards away, a wounded Chinese soldier tried to raise himself, then fell back in painful misery. Chamberlin watched a few minutes and thought of his torment. What difference did it make—life or death? But why should a man suffer? He took careful aim with his carbine and fired. The Chinese soldier suffered no more.

Dead men lay along the trench. Outside the trench the bloody stump of a leg stuck out of the sand. Other bits of bodies and equipment were scattered in and mixed with the dirt.

There was no sign of any officers from I Company. A black corporal seemed to be in charge.

Wounded men lay in a pile. Chamberlin wondered why. Was it for warmth? He had heard that when a man loses blood and goes into shock he gets cold, even in hot weather. One man's head was a ball of bloody bandages. Another had a hole in his thigh as big as a man's fist. It was open to the hot sun. Flies were crawling on it. Each time a member of the pile moved. The man with the wounded head cried out in pain. The medics had no painkiller left. There were no more bandages or blood plasma. One medic wept; another slept. They could do no more.

The lad with the hole in his leg called to Chamberlin. "Hey, mac, give me a hand, will you?"

"Sure, son. What can I do for you?"

As Chamberlin came closer, the lad said, "I have to urinate. Can you help me get up?"

Chamberlin tried. The man with the head wound cried out in pain. It was no use. It could not be done without creating pain for him. After many patient attempts, Chamberlin gave up.

"To hell with it," he said helplessly. "Why don't you let it go where you are?"

"I can't do that."

"Well, damn it, I can't help you without hurting the other guys." Frustration filled Chamberlin's voice.

Chamberlin moved away from failure. But he watched from a short distance. He witnessed a great example of determination. The lad, whom he could not help, ever so slowly extricated himself from the pile of flesh, painfully rose to his feet, moved a few feet away from his wounded companions, and urinated in the most modest, meticulous manner possible.

The day passed slowly. Men from non-fighting units made trip after trip to carry back the wounded and dead. Lieutenant Burke from Headquarters Company was Lieutenant Pierce's best friend. When he heard that Pierce was missing, he had already been bringing out supplies and carrying back wounded for over twenty-four hours. With no rest, he voluntarily continued searching the battlefield for another twenty-four hours for his friend. But even this devotion was not sufficient against the relentless forces of fate. What can devotion do against death? Pierce was never found.

General "Bulldog" Smith, Assistant Division Commander, flew up to the front in his helicopter. He looked like a bulldog: short, squat, and fat. He tried to look and act tough. His whirlybird settled near where Burke and his men were lining up the dead bodies.

When Burke reported to him Smith said, "I want to talk to some of the fighting boys."

Burke led him to the dead. Slowly he turned back the blankets from silent faces. "There they are, Sir," he said. "Talk to them."

The general looked at death. He looked into the eyes of Burke. He saw no disrespect; only sad, weary, helpless resignation, all masking a silent anger, not at Smith, but at this damn war. Smith turned, hurried back to his helicopter and sped back to division headquarters.

Lieutenant Burke covered the faces of the dead and set out again toward Eerie in an agonizing quest. He knew the truth, but he refused to believe.

In the morning Sergeant Baker brought out more supplies. He found only the weapons platoon, wounded and dead on the hill.

"Where the hell is everybody?" he asked Sergeant Joe Penscock.

"Moroney took the rest of the company out to rescue I Company," said Penscock.

"Where's Pierce and the other officers?"

"Pierce is missing. He led a counterattack when the Chinks broke through our perimeter last night. He was last seen charging the little bastards. Buckhuyt's dead. Price was wounded. They took him back. Chamberlin's with Moroney."

As they talked, propellor-driven Navy attack planes flew low over Eerie and dropped their 500-pound bombs on the remnants of L Company there. Baker and Penscock saw the bombs leave the plane. They hit the dirt. The bombs tore up the top of the hill and added to the many craters already there. Miraculously there were no casualties from this accident of war, except to the morale of the men. What the hell could they expect next.

The men out on T-Bone saw the bombing. Anger at the Marine pilots who flew the planes rose up in them. If the planes had made another run there were promises of hostile fire from the friendly troops. There was a question whether the nylon marking panels had been put out.

In frustration Sergeant Penscock yelled out as if to the errant pilots, "We can't fight the whole damn world!"

Baker reported to battalion headquarters that there were no officers on Eerie and asked for instructions. He was told to gather up the remainder of the men—the whole, the wounded and the dead, and return to the MLR. He and Penscock carried out those orders.

At last, toward dusk, L Company was relieved. Chamberlin was the last man to move down the slope. He helped a litter team carry a wounded man on a stretcher. It was the big boy who had had to urinate.

"Glad you made it, son." Chamberlin spoke almost in a whisper.

The lad turned his head toward the voice. "So am I," he answered sincerely. He recognized the man who had tried to help him. Suddenly it dawned on him. This was no ordinary soldier. What it was that told he could not say. Some men wore their rank in combat and some did not. This man did not. But he must be an officer. And he had called him "Mac." It became very important to correct that error.

"Sorry I called you 'Mac,' Sir," he apologized. It sounded stupid as soon as he said it. He had meant no disrespect. Why should he feel obliged to prove it? Maybe he was not an officer after all.

"That's okay, son."

When they rounded the bend in the road and were again safe behind the hill from the enemy, Chamberlin felt a great weariness creep over his body. He sat by the road and rested.

7

They rested. They were safe, tired, and happy. Happy to be alive. Life was precious to them now because it had been so precarious. They had seen death and pain. Now they were glad because death had not chosen them. Chamberlin had experienced peaks of pleasure. His first orgasm, first sexual intercourse with a woman, his wedding night, becoming a father, graduations, getting his commission, things like that were exciting moments. But they were naught compared to the feeling that now overwhelmed him of just being alive.

The place they went to was like home. It was the place where Chamberlin had joined the company. Platoons and squads returned to the same areas they had so recently left. Buddies pitched their pup tents on the same patches of soil. They rested in a peace marred only by sorrow at the loss of their comrades in war.

Chamberlin fought sorrow. The reality of war told him that many might die. What could he do? Sorrow would not bring them back. Dawes had been a damn good soldier. But he was dead now. They were lucky that more had not been killed.

Bodies and minds recuperated with food, rest, and security. Equipment was replaced or refurbished. Administrative duties were tended to.

Some talked about the battle; others repressed it. Chamberlin encouraged his men to talk. He was proud of his men and talked openly of what they had done.

Chamberlin recommended Neathery, Vincent, and Browne for Bronze Stars for Valor because of what they had done on Dagmar. And when Chamberlin attended a battalion staff meeting, Major Moore commended him for it. Moore said that decorations were a boost to morale and that officers should be on the alert for acts of gallantry. He expected that there would be some recommendations for awards as a result of the action on T-Bone. He suggested that anyone who stood his ground and fought off the enemy warranted at least a Bronze Star.

When Chamberlin rose to give the report on his company, all eyes were on him. His fatigues were clean but they were not pressed or well-fitted as most officers' fatigues were. He had swapped his battle-dirtied uniform for a clean, unpressed one at the field shower, the same as the enlisted men did. He wore no insignia of rank. Around his neck and tucked into his fatigue jacket was an olive-drab, GI towel to soak up the sweat and keep out the dust. His garb was impressive in the sense that it seemed out of place amid a group of officers. Nor were his words of great note. In fact, he seemed nervous, almost as if he felt out of place.

Colonel Spottswood noted the sharp contrast in Chamberlin's appearance now from what it had been when he first reported to him. He studied Chamberlin. He fancied himself a student of human behavior. Chamberlin was different all right. Spottswood noted the slim, thong-girded thighs and twin daggers. Leather thongs were a division taboo. General Ruffner did not like them. Chamberlin's carbine was encased in the dust flap of a fatigue jacket to keep the dust off it, another violation of regulations. Spottswood wondered if Chamberlin was strong enough to pay the price for his defiance of rules and tradition. He thought of Socrates, Caesar, and Lincoln. They, too, had been different. Each had paid a price. And then, there was Christ. Spottswood did not speak to Chamberlin about any of these things. He had heard of Chamberlin's performance on T-Bone. He wondered, *Was there a price for valor, also?*

Upon his return to the company, Chamberlin called a squad leader's meeting. It was decided to put everyone in his platoon in for a decoration for the action on Eerie, except Sergeants Sides and Amos. Neathery, Browne, and Dawes were recommended for Silver Stars, the rest for Bronze Stars.

Sides and Amos, not being squad leaders, were not at the meeting. They knew what was going on, but they had no complaints. They chose to remain silent. After all, what could they say?

It never occurred to Chamberlin that anyone would recommend him for an award. It would be nice to be decorated for heroism, he thought. Why had he not done more?

"How are you coming with the recommendations?" Chamberlin asked the company clerk, Corporal Arnold Schiefer.

"Well, we've got the ones for Dagmar done," replied Schiefer.

"How about the ones I put in for Eerie?"

"We're working on Pierce's, Moroney's and yours first."

"You mean somebody put me in for an award?" Chamberlin asked with boyish surprise.

Schiefer smiled. "We weren't supposed to tell you, Sir."

Chamberlin smiled and felt warm and good inside.

For a few days he did not press Schiefer about the recommendations for his men.

Knox dug out a thong and tied down his bayonet scabbard. He wanted to copy Chamberlin's style.

"The whole platoon ought to do this," he said. "Then we'd be a special outfit."

Browne saw him. Raw rage roared forth. "Take that fucking leather thong off! Don't you know that's against orders?"

A surprised Knox looked at Browne. "But that fucking Chamberlin wears 'em," he said artlessly.

Browne reached out with his crooked left arm and grabbed a fist full of Knox's fatigue jacket. He hauled him up tight. "His name is Lieutenant Chamberlin and don't ever let me hear you call him anything else. Hear? And he's the only one in this damn platoon who wears thongs unless he says so."

Maybe he could not put it in words, but Knox understood what Browne meant. And, he suddenly realized, it made sense. Nobody could copy Chamberlin.

Browne released Knox, turned and walked away. Knox took the thong off his bayonet scabbard.

Browne retreated to the privacy of his pup tent. He pondered his outburst as he lay face downward on his sack. He closed his eyes. The vision of Chamberlin walking among his men in the darkness of night combat crossed his mental screen. *Damn it, when I see a man in combat with leather thongs tied around his thighs, I want that man to be Lieutenant Chamberlin, not just anybody,* he thought.

Time passed. Lieutenant Moroney, now the company commander, asked Chamberlin to hold classes for the men.

"What do you want me to teach them?"

"Teach them anything you want to. Whatever you think is most useful."

Chamberlin had been in charge of bayonet training and unarmed combat when he was an instructor at Fort Dix. He had learned his lessons well from his cadre. So now he taught the men flat-blade bayonet. After having mastered the cumbersome Army method, he had learned how to really use a bayonet from an officer who had learned it from the famed Colonel Biddle of the USMC.

"It's simple," he said. "Never stick an enemy with a bayonet because it takes too long to pull it out. During that time you are vulnerable. Instead, keep your rifle at high port, parry the enemy's bayonet down, and smash the side of his head with a horizontal butt stoke."

He taught them how to use knives and how to protect themselves when unarmed. He taught them what he had learned from Neathery—to swear and holler in a firefight. And in a soft, subdued style to which they listened in sharp silence, he spoke to them about fear, courage, and caring for their comrades.

Somebody had to write letters to the relatives of those who were killed on Eerie. Moroney asked Chamberlin to write to the parents of Lieutenant Buckhuyt. He said he would write to Lieutenant Pierce's wife.

Chamberlin thought about Pierce. He wished he had known him better. They had not talked much. Once they had compared dreams about their sons. Pierce had bragged that little Jimmy was going to be a football player. He had boasted that Rocky (he had already nicknamed his newborn son) was going to be a baseball player.

Chamberlin did not know Lieutenant Buckhuyt well either, but he wrote as nice a letter as he could to his parents. He also wrote to the parents of Melnie Dawes extolling his courage and heroic deeds. He knew that everybody hoped death would come with little or no suffering and, if it came in combat, with honor. He tried to camouflage the pain and trauma and highlight the courage. That was easy with Dawes. It was more difficult with Buckhuyt.

Lieutenant Price had been sent back to a MASH unit after the battle for Eerie. For a few days L Company had only two officers, Moroney and Chamberlin. Then two new second lieutenants, Eugene Porter and Allan Fanjoy, joined the company. Moroney assigned Porter to the Weapons Platoon and Fanjoy to the Third Platoon.

Chamberlin treated the new officers much as he had been treated a few short weeks ago. He was friendly but did not say too much to them. They would have to prove themselves like everybody else. True friendship over here, he now knew, did not depend on how you acted under normal conditions, but how you performed when your guts were exposed. He felt very close to Moroney and the men in his Second Platoon.

Chamberlin missed his family more now. He wished he could cuddle his wife, Jo, at night. He longed to see his precious three-year-old, Judy Joy again and his new son, Rocky. He missed his mother, his three brothers and his sister—especially his brother Willard. He wrote letters to his wife, his mother, and Willard. There was no censorship of mail like in World War II, so he told them of the battle on Eerie. He told them of losing one of his daggers, and of playing baseball with grenades. He told them that he missed them and loved them very much.

8

In a single line they filed around the base of the hill. They maintained an interval of two or three yards between men, close enough for whispered messages and far enough so that few could be the victims of the same hostile fire. They tried to step silently for this was no-man's-land. Little things, like the rubbing of pant leg against pant leg, the touch of metal against metal, the scuff of a foot, sounded sharply against the stillness. The men thought that these sounds could be heard far away, and they were afraid. They tried harder to proceed quietly.

It was an eerie night. The moon was bright. Large, dark clouds moved slowly across the sky, giving an alternating effect of pitch blackness and naked brightness as they covered and uncovered the moon. In the brightness the fear of getting lost was less, but the fear of being seen was greater. Which was worse depended upon the individual.

Off to the left front the rounded dome of Baldy was silhouetted against the sky. To the front and right front more jagged ridges and peaks leaned against the horizon during the moonlight. Out there the valley floor narrowed and wound between two ridge lines to spread out further beyond. In the ridge to the right front was another shallower cut. Through these and the valley surrounding Baldy to the left the Chinese could sneak and attack either the outposts on these terrain features or the main line to the rear.

The mission tonight was to set up three listening posts at key points to warn of the approach of enemy forces.

At a prearranged spot Sergeant Browne's squad peeled off from the rest and went a little to the left. They took up a position in the middle of the valley. The rest of the men were to continue on, half to each of the approaches ahead.

Chamberlin went with Browne and his squad. After they were positioned and all was quiet he waited awhile with them. In the dry grass creatures of the night stirred and made weird noises.

"Halt! Who goes there?" a nervous voice spoke too loudly.

"Shut up!" somebody whispered.

In the moonlight Chamberlin looked out over the valley floor at the hills around. Their mission had been carefully explained to him by a young lieutenant from S2. His feelings tonight were much different from those he had experienced on Dagmar during his first taste of combat, Korean style. Tonight the mission took precedence over his fear. The fear was there, perhaps as much as ever, but now he knew how he reacted to danger. Cool and confident. If the Chinese came he would calmly report to Battalion on the radio. If it were a small group they would ambush them. Maybe he could even stick one of them with his dagger. If it were a large group they would withdraw. He felt battle-hardened, confident, cocky. He was a damn good platoon leader and had a damn good platoon. His men knew what they were doing and would never let him down. He had briefed them well. There was no doubt in his mind about their accomplishing their mission.

69

After a brief stay with this listening post, Chamberlin and his radio man, Cottrell, set out to check the other two posts. First they went to the post on the right. They found the place easily enough. But there was no one there.

"Where the hell are they?" whispered Chamberlin.

"Maybe they went farther," offered Cottrell.

Thinking they might have misunderstood, Chamberlin led on through the cut into the valley beyond. There was no listening post to be found.

Could they have been ambushed? But there had been no sound of a firefight, no signal of distress. Each group was equipped with a walkie-talkie. If there had been trouble they would have reported it.

"Let's go to the other post," said Chamberlin more loudly than before.

He did not know whether he was angry or not. Certainly he was disturbed. The Chinks could have poured through the gap with no one the wiser, and his men would have been to blame. No, he would have been to blame.

They followed the base of the ridge to where the other post was supposed to be stationed. Nobody was there either. They went further out into the valley toward the enemy lines. Chamberlin was angry now, and worried, too.

"Son-of-a-bitch, where in hell are they?" he mumbled as they returned through the gap toward the place where the men were supposed to be. "Somebody must have fucked up."

"Lieutenant Chamberlin, over here." The low whisper came from the black, sheer wall of hill to their left.

They recognized the voice of Sergeant McAfee. Chamberlin and Cottrell moved quickly into the large, dark cave housing the men of both listening posts.

"What the hell are you doing here?" demanded Chamberlin.

"We got lost," murmured McAfee.

Chamberlin's anger at their failure was diluted with relief at their safety. What good would it do to be angry or punitive?

"Are you all here?" It was too dark to see.

"Yes, Sir."

The night was now nearly over. Too late to worry about the listening posts now. The Chinese would never come at this hour. In a little while they went back.

L Company had moved onto the front lines again on 22 June. Now they were in a position on a long ridge opposite a bare dome of terrain called "Baldy." Baldy was one of the outposts taken in operation "Counter." It had been switching hands between the Chinese and Americans since then. Men fought, suffered, and died over a silly piece of geography. General Ruffner was building his reputation and bucking for another star to put him in line for a staff job.

How in hell could my men get lost, thought Chamberlin, as he pondered about the patrol. *Harry and I didn't get lost. But what can I do about it? Their blame is my blame. I am responsible. I didn't have to stay back with the first listening post. I could have gone on and stationed each one. I can't very well do anything about it, or even chew them out without looking silly myself. I'm not much good at chewing out people anyhow, especially people I care about. But, by Jesus, next time I'll make sure there are no slip-ups!*

Chamberlin's patrol report was short and simple. Mission accomplished.

On the nights 24 June and 25 June, there was a fierce

firefight on Porkchop as the Chinese tried to dislodge the American forces there. Porkchop, so named because of its shape, was Hill 266 on the war maps. It was situated between Baldy on its left and Eerie on its right. It was another one of the outposts taken in operation "Counter." It was now occupied by a rifle platoon from K Company. During the night, communications were lost with them. On the morning of 25 June it was not known if there were any survivors or even who now held the hill.

L Company was ordered to send out a combination reconnaissance and rescue patrol to determine who occupied the outpost and to bring back any wounded or dead Americans they found.

The First Platoon was given this tedious, dangerous mission. Lieutenant Price, who had recently rejoined the company, and Platoon Sergeant Bill Browne led their platoon out across the valley floor and up the rear slope of Porkchop as their anxious L Company comrades watched from the MLR.

One was more anxious than most. That was his older brother out there. Bob Browne watched through field glasses as his brother Bill progressed up the hill. He had no trouble picking out his brother. He knew his every move and idiosyncrasy. At Bob's side were Jack Neathery and Lieutenant Chamberlin. Both Jack and Bob had had a few beers that morning. Where they got it, Chamberlin did not know. But it was not uncommon for the men on the MLR to drink a little, if they could get it, in an attempt to drown their sorrows. So it was generally tolerated as long as it did not get out of hand.

Anyhow, the beer made Bob even more concerned for his brother Bill and less reasonable about his own behavior.

Those watching saw the patrol take some mortar

rounds in their midst. They saw bits of dirt disturbed by bursts of small-arms fire. They saw the men hit the dirt. They could not tell whether they were wounded or just taking cover. Maybe they were dead. But not all of them at least, for they got up and continued up the hill.

Bob Browne was beside himself with fear for his brother. Drunken courage welled up within him. "I've got to go out there and help Bill," he cried. "He needs me."

"You can't go out there all alone," Neathery told him.

"I'm going to, and you can't stop me," bellowed Browne. "You're only a damned PFC, you don't tell me what to do."

"Then I'm going with you," replied Neathery, seeming to ignore Browne's insult. "You damn fools will get yourselves killed if I don't take care of you."

Chamberlin spoke in a low, slow voice. "Bob, Jack, you're not going anywhere. There's nothing you can do."

Bob Browne and Jack Neathery stayed where they were.

Out on Porkchop, the patrol completed its mission. They swept the hill. They found a few of K Company's men alive and still in possession of the outpost. They also found several wounded and dead. They brought these back in addition to their own casualties. Among the latter was Lieutenant Price. His football dreams were shot to hell. Platoon Sergeant Bill Browne, who a few days ago had been only a squad leader, was again without a platoon leader. Promotions and responsibilities came fast in combat to those with the brains and guts to bear them.

At noon chow on 27 June some new replacements

were assigned to the Second Platoon. They were young, earnest, mostly scared men—some white and some black. The Army had done a good job with integration since World War II. Two boys from Kentucky, Carl Fields and John Partin, wanted to be assigned to the same squad because they were buddies.

"We take care of each other," explained Fields, who was known as "Kentucky."

"I don't think Kentucky could get along without me, said Partin. "He's not very bright. The only one who loves him is his mother and I promised her I'd take care of him." A faint smile creased Partin's face as he spoke.

Chamberlin smiled too. Kentucky was very homely. He had big ears, a small, twisted nose, and floppy lips that covered yellowish-brown, irregular teeth. He was very short.

Kentucky said, "With a face like mine, you're lucky if even your mother loves you."

The men around laughed at Kentucky's sense of humor. Kentucky didn't smile.

"How come you let Partin make fun of you, Kentucky?" asked Browne.

"I'm on duty today. It's his day off. I have to do all the work and take all his shit today."

"What do you mean?"

"You better let me explain about these two," announced another new man, Jack Tally. "All three of us are from Kentucky and went through basic together. Kentucky and Partin have an agreement. One day one is on duty and the next day the other one takes over. The one that's on duty has to do all the work while the other one fucks off if he can get away with it. They both drink like hell, but the one on duty never gets drunk. If you can keep 'em together, Sir, they'd be a lot better off."

Chamberlin had a thing about drinking on the front lines, especially after the episode with Browne and Neathery a couple days ago.

"They can't drink up here on the line," he said seriously.

"They'll drink if there's any liquor around," Tally said simply.

There was not time to press the point. A messenger asked Chamberlin to report to Moroney. L Company had to relieve F Company on Baldy.

Chamberlin assigned the replacements quickly. Partin and Kentucky went to Browne's squad.

Moroney decided to place the Second Platoon on the left of Baldy, the Third Platoon in the middle, and the First Platoon on the right. Since they would be moving onto the hill from the right and the Second Platoon would have the farthest to go, the order of march was second, third, and first. Units of the Weapons Platoon were attached to each rifle platoon. Moroney wanted to be with the lead platoon, so he asked Chamberlin to bring up the rear and join his platoon after they were in position.

Moroney's orders were simple. Go over the top of the hill and take up positions on the slope facing the enemy. If they could not get on the forward slope, dig trenches forward to the forward slope. Whatever happened, he wanted the men in these key defensive positions before dark. This way they could see the Chinese coming and negate any element of surprise. There seemed to be no question about them coming.

Chamberlin told his men what to do. He did not like being separated from them. After the patrol fiasco he felt that his presence was needed to get things done right. But he did what Moroney told him to do.

Shortly after the company had started to move out, Browne called Chamberlin on the radio. "What am I supposed to do with White? He won't go. He just sat down on the ground and started bawling. I can't do anything with him."

Chamberlin made a quick decision. "Leave him there. We can't fuck around with him now."

Chamberlin did not know much about White. He remembered him as being a big, well-built, handsome black man. When he got to where White was, White was still sitting by the side of the trail. His head was in his arms and he was still sobbing. Chamberlin did not see White again until he returned from Baldy two days later. In the meantime, whenever White entered his thoughts, there was a strange mixture of anger and pity, not hatred or prejudice, just anger and pity, mostly pity. He knew what the penalty was for refusing to obey an order in combat. It called for a General Court-Martial, with the maximum penalty death by firing squad. *But what the hell good would punishment do, he thought. Besides, I didn't take any action against my men who failed to carry out their mission on the patrol. Was White any more guilty than they? Nor did anyone do anything about my refusal to stay on Dagmar when things got too hot. Was White any more cowardly that I was then? And White was from Louisiana where white men did not give black men much chance to develop confidence and courage.*

9

F Company left Baldy before L Company was in position. Men scrambled hastily out of their foxholes and dashed over the top of the hill for safety. They did not wait for orders. Who needed orders at a time like this? All they wanted to do was get the hell out of there. Of course the Chinese saw them silhouetting themselves on the skyline and harassed them with small-arms fire and occasional mortar rounds.

Chamberlin herded the rear elements of his company through the weary, relieved men of F Company. At the foot of Baldy he told Sergeant Bill Browne to take over getting his platoon into position. Then he joined his own platoon on the left side of Baldy.

The Second Platoon had not made it to the forward slope of the hill. Bullets snapped overhead. The men were prostrated on the ground, some digging, some just hugging the earth for protection.

Bob Browne saw Chamberlin coming and moved down the slope a few yards to meet him.

"That damn Sides has got the men all nerved up," reported Browne. "He's so damn jumpy. I can't do anything with my men."

"Did anybody get on the forward slope?" asked Chamberlin.

"Only Jackson, with a machine-gun."

"Is he all right?"

"We don't know. Everything is all screwed up. F Company didn't wait for us to get here before they bugged out. Nobody knows what the hell they're doing. I think I'm going to crack up, myself."

Chamberlin answered with soft confidence. "Oh, you're not going to crack up, Bob. You're a good squad leader. Don't worry about Jim. He's awful close to rotation. He's got reason to be jumpy."

By then Chamberlin and Browne had moved up next to some of Browne's men. Browne continued. "He's got the First Squad where you wanted the Third Squad."

"Where's the Third Squad?"

"I don't know. Over on the left somewhere. They were supposed to be on the right."

"Where's Harry?"

"He was with the Third Squad when we left. He probably stayed with McAfee."

"I wanted him over here on the right where I'm going to have my CP." Chamberlin was getting a little perturbed now. He did not want to be without communications.

Browne was calming now. "I know. But like I said, Sides got everybody confused."

"What the hell difference does it make?" drawled a nearby lad who was sitting on the ground nonchalantly smoking a cigarette. "We're all here, ain't we?"

Chamberlin recognized Kentucky, one of the new replacements. Kentucky continued, "Lieutenant, you want me to go over the top of the hill and look after Jackson and the machine-gun?"

As Chamberlin debated an answer, Partin, who was lying on the ground nearby spoke up, "You can't leave. You're supposed to be digging me a foxhole, you lazy bastard."

"I ain't going to dig no fucking foxhole here. The lieutenant said we're going over the other side of the hill to shoot some Chinks. It don't make no sense to dig in here."

Listening to Kentucky and Partin argue eased the tension. "How are you new fellows doing?" he asked.

"I'm awful damn dry," said Kentucky. "Got a drink, Sir?"

Thinking that Kentucky had probably drunk all his water already, Chamberlin offered him his canteen, despite the inappropriateness of the request. Kentucky unscrewed the cap and sniffed the contents. He made a wry face.

"Shit, Lieutenant, I thought you might have some liquor." Kentucky handed the canteen back to him.

"We don't drink on the front lines," Brown said to Kentucky rather sharply. "The lieutenant doesn't need liquor for courage."

"Neither do I, but I sure need it when I'm dry," answered Kentucky.

A mortar round landed close and interrupted any rebuke that Browne may have intended. He hit the dirt in a spontaneous reaction. Chamberlin crouched to one knee. His eyes brightened as he scanned the men around him to see if any were hit. Kentucky remained sitting unperturbed. After a moment Chamberlin stood up. He walked a few feet away, turned his back and urinated. Kentucky rose, strolled casually to the side of the lieutenant and followed his example.

Hot ire rose in Browne. *Of all the damn arrogance,* he thought. *A raw-assed rookie pissing side by side with an officer! I'll straighten that little son-of-a-bitch out.*

Turning back to Browne, Chamberlin said, "Looks like you got some good men here." He put his arm around Kentucky's shoulders. "They don't seem scared at all."

Browne's resolution faltered. What could he say now?

"What the hell's there to be scared of?" asked Kentucky. "This ain't half as dangerous as running a still back home."

"What do you want us to do?" asked Browne, thinking he would take care of Kentucky the first chance he got.

"Send a man over to make contact with the Third Squad. Tell them to keep contact with your left flank, dig in enough to protect themselves and move to the forward slope as soon as it starts getting dark. You do the same here. I'll tell the First Squad and then be back. The squads might as well stay where they are. It doesn't make that much difference. My CP will be behind your squad." Chamberlin paused a moment. "Why don't you send Kentucky? He seems to want something to do."

"I'll go," volunteered Kentucky. "It'll give me a chance to see if Tally's all right."

"Can I go with him?" asked Partin. "He's so stupid he'll probably get lost. I have to start looking after him in a few minutes anyhow."

"Send 'em both if you want to," Chamberlin said to Browne. He also addressed Partin whom he had perceived to be the brighter of the two. "When you come back, bring Harry Cottrell, my radioman, with you."

Chamberlin went to where the First Squad was. He told them what to do. His calm soothed the men. He crawled to the crest of the hill and hollered at Jackson.

"Where are you, Cecil? You all right?"

Sergeant Jackson stuck his head out of a hole. "Over here, Sir. I'm okay."

Chamberlin saw where Jackson was and that he was really all right. He was only a few yards away and in a good position. A tripod, a swap with F Company, was in position on a shelf-like ledge of a large, crew-sized foxhole.

"You got the machine-gun?" asked Chamberlin.

"Yes, Sir. I got it in the hole with me."

"Good idea. Keep it clean. We'll be over with you as soon as we can."

"I sure hope so, Sir."

The valley surrounding Baldy spread out north perhaps 300 yards. Connecting the higher peaks of the north (where the enemy was) with Baldy was a narrow ridge forming a saddle. It seemed like the most feasible route between the two. Chamberlin decided to place a listening post out about a hundred yards in front of Browne's squad at a point where the ridge started to slope toward the seat of the saddle. From there they could best hear movements in the valleys to the right, to the left, and along the ridge. He noticed that the machine-gun where Jackson was could cover the right side of the saddle and the valley in front of it. He hoped the machine-gun attached to the Third Squad could cover the left side of this approach.

Chamberlin returned to his CP. He told Browne where he wanted the listening post. Then he waited for dusk. He dug a little. But, like Kentucky had said, there was not much sense in digging here.

He remembered that he had not had time to read a letter that had come just before they left for Baldy. Glancing at the return address had told him it was another one from Ruby. No rush about reading it. He opened it now. Its sweet scent seemed out of place on the battlefield. She wrote the usual sweet shit. He put the letter in his jacket pocket and carefully buttoned the flap. Was this an unconscious act to hide her? He wondered, if he got killed, would his wife get Ruby's letter with his personal effects. The irony of life—or death.

With dusk the men moved over the top of the hill and took up defensive positions on the forward slope. Browne sent Neathery and Virgil Johnson, another recent black replacement, out to be the ears of the platoon at the listening post.

Chamberlin set out to check his men to see if they were all right, had enough ammunition (not that he could do much about it if they didn't) and were ready to fight. His greatest concern was Jackson out there alone. He went there first.

The .30 caliber, air-cooled machine-gun sat majestically in position. A silent sentinel, her sights were aimed just to the right of the listening post in front of Browne's squad. She was clean, well-adjusted, and ready to burst into action at a touch. Her insides: bolt, barrel extension, barrel, and cover group had been checked and rechecked by her master and keeper, Sergeant Jackson. Her head space, an adjustment made by screwing the barrel just so far into the barrel extension, was precisely accurate. This had to be exactly right for her to fire without malfunctioning. She was firmly locked in place on her tripod by two vise-like clamps. These prevented her from swiveling sideways or up and down. On the right of the tripod was a dial to rotate her muzzle right or left, one mil per click. Underneath the receiver was a similar dial for up-and-down manipulation. While locked in place, she could be brought from a reference point onto specific, predetermined targets in the dark by counting the horizontal and vertical clicks. The legs of her tripod were sandbagged in place to keep her stable. At her side was a wooden ammunition crate. Four 250-round belts had been linked together and lay neatly folded in the box. One end of the belt had been fed into the left side of her receiver. She was loaded and ready to spit death at the rate of 400 rounds per minute. Another box of 1,000 rounds was nearby in the foxhole.

Sergeant Jackson was a good soldier. He always did what his superiors told him to. Therefore he had scrambled over the top of Baldy to the forward slope when they first got out there. Bullets whistling close by scared him, but they did not deter him. Being the lead man of the Second Platoon, he did not notice the others falter until it was too late to turn back. With him he had carried the machine-gun. He had kept her covered and in the foxhole with him until dusk. Then he had mounted her on the tripod and prepared her for action.

Now, as darkness blanketed Baldy, the First Squad, what was left of it after Eerie, Jackson's ammunition bearer, and Sergeant Sides joined Jackson and his gun in the hole. Soon they saw the shadowy silhouette of Chamberlin striding casually toward them. Holding it at the balance, he carried his carbine loosely in his right hand. He had replaced the regular fifteen-round clip with four thirty-round clips, staggered top to bottom, and taped together. Now he had 120 rounds at his fingertips. He could fire thirty-rounds, release the clip, flip it over, reinsert it and fire thirty more, continuing this until the full 120 rounds had been expended in less than one minute if the piece was on full automatic.

Chamberlin lowered himself into the foxhole. "Everybody all right?" he asked.

"Yes, Sir," answered Jackson.

"How's the machine-gun? Ready to go?"

"I think so, Sir. I kept it as clean as I could."

"How much ammo you got?"

"F Company left us a thousand rounds and we brought another thousand, Sir."

Suddenly some muffled whispers coming from the right front in a foreign dialect, Chinese or Korean, quieted the men in the foxhole. An enemy grenade exploded near the lip of the hole. The men instinctively cowered close to the bottom of their cover. Fear gripped and paralyzed them.

After a moment's hesitation during which he thought somebody should do something but nobody did, Chamberlin snapped, "Where are your fucking grenades? Somebody give me a grenade."

A body handed Chamberlin a grenade. He stood erect, pulled the pin and tossed it where he thought the whispers had come from. Then he stepped behind the machine-gun, loosened her clamps and fired a burst in the direction of likely retreat for the whisperers.

"Sons-a-bitches. I hope I got 'em," he muttered. Then he relaid the machine-gun on her primary target and clamped her tight.

As if the machine-gun fire were a signal and her tracers a guide, enemy artillery opened up. Shells rained down on Baldy. Fortunately, most of them landed on the crest or the rear slope. Perhaps the Chinks thought the Americans were still back there. But enough of them fell among the foxholes where the men were to put the fear of instant death or permanent crippling in them. It was worse than Eerie. The concussion of the close ones would seem to almost lift the men out of their holes.

Like clouds above portended rain, so the falling shells portended the coming of Chinese foot soldiers. The clouds formed an umbrella over the land and made

it darker. The barrage covered Baldy and made it dead-
lier. The poor damn Communist bastards! They would
have to come. They would have to be slaughtered. Even
now they were out there moving forward under cover of
the barrage. They would be ready to assault as soon as
the artillery moved its strike zone further back.

"Got any phosphorous grenades?" shouted Chamberlin over the din. "If you have, get some out there so
we can see. Tell Headquarters to get some flares up."

Somebody tossed a few phosphorous grenades out
front. They lit up a small area. Webster, now the First
Squad leader, relayed Chamberlin's orders to Headquarters over the walkie-talkie. Soon the company's 60-mm
mortars had flares in the air, lighting the battlefield
below as they parachuted slowly to the ground. In rapid
succession, larger and longer-burning flares from 81-mm
and 4.2 mortars and supporting artillery units joined
them. Before the night was over, B-26 planes took to the
air and circled over the battle arena, dropping their spar-
klers that burst forth in multiple stars of light and spent
a long, lovely time floating to earth. During the entire
night there was very little darkness in front of Baldy.

Through this light the enemy had to come. Those
were their orders. They had no choice. They had not visited Baldy for two days. Now they would pay their re-
spects. They must overrun, capture men and weapons,
and rout the decadent, imperialist Americans. They
must kill, kill, kill! In their pre-attack pep rally they had
promised their political commanders what they would
do to the American dogs.

Chamberlin saw them first. "Somebody get on the
gun," he ordered. "Here they come. Tell Browne to get
the LP back."

The Chinese came jogging along the crest of the saddle toward the listening post and Browne's squad. Chamberlin hoped that Neathery and Johnson had pulled back soon enough.

Jackson took over the machine-gun. She was already aimed at the oncoming Chinks. He fired a burst, lowered his head below the rim of the foxhole, rotated the gun two clicks to the right, peeked again, and fired another short burst, following a prearranged firing plan.

Jesus Christ, thought Chamberlin, *the Chinks will be on top of Browne's men in no time if Jackson keeps firing like that.* "Let me take the gun," he said. "You watch the ammunition and keep it feeding, Cecil." He did not want to hurt Jackson's feelings but he did not want the Chinks to overrun his platoon either. Now was no time for sensitivity.

In training, men were neither taught nor allowed to fire a free-swinging gun. It was too dangerous and scattered the bullets around too much to be effective, they were told. They were warned not to believe everything you read in books or see in movies. They learned to pull the trigger with the left index finger, turn the horizontal dial with their right hand and the vertical dial with their left hand. To keep the barrel from overheating and to conserve ammunition they should fire short bursts of four or five rounds.

But during World War II, Chamberlin had also had training on .50-caliber machine guns at Fort Bliss, Texas, when he was in an antiaircraft outfit. They used to fire at targets towed behind airplanes. The machine-guns were free-swinging and they aimed them by watching the flight of their tracers.

Now this training came in handy. He loosened the gun all the way. He pulled the trigger with his right middle finger. His left hand on top of the receiver guided the stream of tracers onto the front-running Chinks. He fired a long burst, thirty or forty rounds, swinging the gun in a slow arc. It jumped a little at first, but added pressure with his left hand and more lift with his right steadied the piece.

From front to rear, the enemy soldiers silhouetted on the skyline of the saddle ridge fell like dominoes. Bullets tore up the dirt around them as Chamberlin warmed to his role. *Aim for the ground just in front of a moving target,* he remembered having learned. *Let the bastards run and fall into the fire.*

"Look at the little bastards drop!" Chamberlin yelled with wild excitement. "We got 'em Cecil. You got this baby firing perfect."

Chamberlin's fear was gone. His adrenaline was flowing forth in agile action, words, and mental alertness. "Come on, you little yellow bastards," he hollered. "Step right up and get a bullet in your balls." It was a high that he had never experienced before—killing the enemy to save himself and his men.

From across the valley a direct-fire weapon, with its concomitant backflash, sent out its lethal missile. How could they miss at such close range and with their target so well pinpointed? The shell smashed into the dirt where the machine-gun was. The machine-gun fire ceased.

10

As soon as an enemy attack had become probable—when Chamberlin had called for flares—American artillery exploded into action. All weapons on the MLR zeroed in on the final protective targets. The approaches to Baldy were saturated with mortar and artillery rounds. No-man's-land became a literal hell, filled more with flying pieces of jagged shrapnel than with enemy soldiers. Shells with proximity fuses exploded as they neared the ground. The cone of dispersion from these spread downward in a larger kill zone than that made by shells with contact fuses. And there was plenty of ammunition. The small, stalemated Korean police action was no great drain on the world's industrial giants, the U.S.A. and the USSR. Thus the opposing forces had no problems keeping their ammo dumps well stocked.

It was estimated that the Chinese forces launched a battalion-sized attack on Baldy that night, supported by at least 3,000 rounds of artillery and mortar fire. That would mean that at least two companies set out to assault the second platoon positions. Since most combat companies were under-strength, there were probably between 200 and 300 enemy troops used in their ill-fated mission of dislodging L Company from the dome of sand. They used only one approach, along the saddle ridge in front of the Second Platoon. To reach any of the other platoons of the company via this avenue they would have had to overrun the Second Platoon first. Most of the attacking forces, of course, never got within sight of the defenders because of the heavy artillery and mortar fire. Those that did make it far enough ran into the withering fire of a charged-up Second Platoon.

But the Chinese soldiers continued to come despite the pounding from American firepower. The law of averages assured that some would get through. And some did. That is, they got through the artillery. They got as far as the Second Platoon. Then they were stopped.

Out at the listening post, Neathery and Johnson had their hands full. They had found a good foxhole and organized their ammunition and equipment so they knew where it was. Johnson was scared. He had not wanted this assignment, but Browne had made him go. Since joining the company a few days before, he had been boastful about his athletic prowess and general manliness. Now in the face of danger he was finding it difficult to live up to expectations. He wished he had kept his mouth shut.

The crew of Chinese sent out to knock out Jackson's machine-gun nest had sneaked through too far to the right for them to notice. So they were still at the LP when the shelling started.

Johnson could no longer control his fear. He jumped out of the foxhole and charged to the rear, screaming, "The Chinese are coming! Neathery's dead! Where's Chamberlin? Where's Chamberlin?"

Johnson was right. The Chinese were coming. As soon as the strike zone of the shelling moved a little to the rear, a Chinese probing patrol came trotting along the ridge toward Neathery, who had stayed at his post. He decided it would be best to slow them down so his comrades would have time to get ready for them. By now some flares had been sent aloft, so the battlefield was dimly lit. He could see the Chinese clearly but they probably could not see him yet. He shot the leading Chink. The bolt of his M1 jammed. Not wanting to be at a disadvantage, he jumped out of his foxhole to meet the foe on a level arena. He remembered what Chamberlin had taught them about never sticking the enemy with your bayonet. It made sense now. He smashed the next victim on the side of the head with a butt stroke. Unfortunately the next Chink was too close and was able to knock Neathery's rifle out of his hands with a butt stroke of his own. Funny, thought Neathery, why don't they shoot me? They must want to take me prisoner. Another glancing blow knocked him to the ground. His hand landed on the handle of an entrenching tool, a short-handled shovel. He swung the shovel as he rose to his feet. It slashed across his assailant's jugular vein. Blood spewed forth from the jagged cleavage. He smashed another under the ear. This one landed in a heap with his head twisted at an awkward angle. His mouth curled in a weird grin. Suddenly those that were rushing toward him started falling as though tripping over an invisible wire. Some rolled a little but mostly they were still. Now he noticed the stream of tracers coming from the right. He retrieved his rifle and hastily withdrew to the rear, realizing that the listening post was no longer needed.

Johnson reached Browne's squad still raving, "Chamberlin! Chamberlin! Where's Chamberlin?"

"He's over there, you yellow, black bastard," Kentucky hollered at him.

Kentucky was not sure if he would have shot him if his rifle had been working. Johnson raced on toward where he had been directed.

Browne welcomed Neathery with open arms. "God,

90

I'm glad you're all right, Jack. I thought you were a goner out there. When we saw Johnson bugging out we thought they got you."

"That was one scared nigger," laughed Neathery. "I couldn't stop him from taking off."

Neathery took up a defensive position a few yards in front of Browne's foxhole. There was no question of his taking a safer spot in the rear. It was his nature to be in the thick of the fight. He never asked for anything less.

The shelling now intensified after those initial probes by the Chinese. A round landed close enough to Neathery's new position to nearly bury him and his equipment. *Must be my lucky day,* he thought as he calmly took off his steel helmet and started digging himself out.

Browne noticed the plight of his buddy and rushed to his aid. In the glare of the flares, the second wave of Chinese could now be seen jogging toward them. He, too, took off his steel helmet to dig. There was nothing else to dig with.

"Are you hit?" asked Browne.

"Of course I'm hit, you stupid bastard," answered Neathery. "Can't you see the dirt all over me?"

As they struggled against time and the Chinese closed in on them, Neathery said to Browne in dead seriousness, "Turn around and smile, Bob. I think there's a photographer from *Stars and Stripes* who wants to take your picture."

Taken off-guard momentarily, Browne did turn his head for a quick glance. He turned back quickly and retorted, "Shut up, you damn asshole, and dig."

Somehow they managed to get Neathery and his M1 unburied before the Chinese were upon them. Browne shot one with his M1. The bolt jammed. He tried to pull it back with his hand, but could not. He put the butt on the ground and kicked the bolt back with his foot. But then it was too late. The Chinks were already there. He did not have time to regrasp his piece in a normal way. Holding it by the end of the barrel, he swung it like a club against the head of the leading foe. Neathery's M1 was clogged with dirt too. He joined Browne in clubbing several more Chinese into oblivion.

Suddenly the machine-gun fire from the right opened up again. The Chinese who were still standing hit the dirt, either from fear or from being hit. Browne and Neathery were now able to withdraw into a smaller defensive circle with their squad.

The difference between life and death, victory or defeat, is often a mere matter of inches. Like the homerun that did not quite clear the fence, the shell aimed at the machine-gun position hit a scant few inches below the muzzle of the gun. It merely blew dirt into Chamberlin's face and momentarily blinded him.

"You dirty, cocksucking motherfucker," muttered Chamberlin, as he spit dirt and wiped his eyes. "Did anybody see his backflash? Keep your eyes open, men, and see if you can spot that bastard."

As the shell struck, Johnson neared the position. Recognizing Chamberlin's voice from perhaps twenty feet away, he dove headlong for the hole and slid in on his belly, much like a long slide into second base.

"You all right?" asked Chamberlin.

"I think I'm hit," answered a shaking Johnson. "My back hurts. I'm bleeding." The blood later turned out to be urine.

"Did Neathery get back?" asked Chamberlin. He was not unconcerned about Johnson, but he was more concerned about Neathery. He respected Neathery for his courage and felt a special bond with him for it. So far Johnson had not bonded with him this way.

"I don't know. I think he's dead," whimpered Johnson.

"Somebody take care of him," ordered Chamberlin as he checked the machine-gun for damage. He yanked the bolt back twice to see if the feeding mechanism worked. Then he fired a short burst. All was well.

Relieved about the machine-gun, Chamberlin worried about Neathery. But there was no time to dwell on death now. He saw more enemy running toward Browne's squad. He mowed them down from front to rear. He was not too worried about hitting his own men, even though he was firing close to them. He could differentiate between friend and foe, for the Chinese did not wear helmets. They wore soft cloth caps. He was confident of his aim.

Suddenly it became almost dark again when most of the flares burned out simultaneously.

"Get some more fucking flares up," ordered Chamberlin, as he peered intently into the darkness.

Flares relit the battlefield just as another round hit a few feet in front of the position. Surrounding its explosion in the brilliant glare was a bazooka squad headed for the machine-gun. The long tube resting on the gunner's shoulder was pointed directly at its goal. Though they seemed to disintegrate in the blast from their own artillery, Chamberlin sent a burst of fire where the squad had been for good measure.

"Look at the stupid bastards," he shouted gleefully. "Shooting their own men. Come on, men, help me pick 'em off. It's like shooting ducks on a pond."

Heads began to appear above the rim of the foxhole next to Chamberlin. Another shell from their persistent antagonist landed close by.

93

"I saw him!" shouted Webster. "Over there."

"So did I," said Chamberlin. "I'll get the motherfuck-er."

He swung the gun to the right and sprayed the area where he had seen the backflash.

"I think you got him," said Sides.

Whether he got him or not, no more shells from that gun bothered them that night.

More enemy troops came along the ridge.

"You guys pick off the singles while I take care of the bunches," suggested Chamberlin. "That way we'll save ammo."

Sides and Webster started picking off targets with their M1 rifles. They became elated with their success. Others in the foxhole joined them. Fear seemed to have almost disappeared. Courage is perhaps equally as contagious as fear.

Sides's rifle jammed. The sand stirred up by the shelling had clogged his piece.

"My damn rifle won't work," he said nervously.

"Piss on it," recommended Chamberlin in complete seriousness. Though urine was not a recommended cleaning solvent, he intuitively knew it would wash the sand out of the working mechanism of a rifle.

"I can't do that, not here," replied a shocked Sides.

"Here, give it to me," Chamberlin said. "I'll piss on it for you."

After this was done, the rifle functioned perfectly.

God, what that man won't do, thought Sides.

Chamberlin wondered how Sergeant McAfee's squad was doing over on the left flank. He worried about Jack Neathery. He knew that the rest of the First Squad and Browne's Second Squad were engaged in the fire-fight and functioning well. He could see them from his

94

position. He hoped for an end to the attack, or at least a lull, so he could check his men. But the shelling never stopped and he felt safer in the foxhole. Nor did the Chinks cease coming for any extended period, and he rationalized that he could accomplish more for his men by manning the machine-gun.

Not long after Neathery and Browne had narrowly escaped being killed or captured by the Chinese, a round exploded within inches of Browne's head. He was knocked unconscious. The explosive force slammed his brain against the back side of his skull. When he came to, he could neither see nor hear. He thought he was dead. Being a staunch Christian, he wondered if this were heaven, hell, or purgatory. It could not be heaven. He hurt too much. But it was not hot enough to be hell. Gradually his thoughts cleared. He hollered but could not hear his voice. Sergeant West came to his aid. A medic also came. Since there was no outward evidence of injury, he was assumed to be okay. The medic went to aid others.

Browne's memory played tricks on him. He forgot that Neathery had alread returned safely from the listening post. "I've got to go help Jack," he screamed.

He tried to leave the foxhole. West grabbed him and pulled him back. "You can't go out there," he yelled. "Jack is okay."

Browne could not hear or see him. He was not sure whether he was alive or dead, but he felt invincible. If he was alive, good. If he was dead, they could not kill him again. In either case, danger lost its deterrence. Even though West was much shorter and lighter than Browne, he managed to get him down and literally sat on him to prevent him from charging blindly into the artillery fire in search of Neathery.

Gradually Browne's senses returned. He could see again and hear a little. He remembered where Jack was. He knew he was not in purgatory. He had a splitting headache.

Over on the left flank of the Second Platoon, McAfee's squad was also engaging the enemy with small-arms fire. Partin and Kentucky had established contact with them earlier. First they found Tally and ascertained that he was all right. Then they located Cottrell and told him that Chamberlin wanted him and his radio over at Chamberlin's CP. The radio had been knocked out of commission. Cottrell was going to go to Chamberlin's CP, but neither Kentucky nor Partin could tell him exactly where it was. McAfee took advantage of the confusion and told Cottrell to stay with his squad. He needed all the help he could get.

After the first shelling and assault which probably lasted about two hours, the shelling began again in earnest. Behind Cottrell's foxhole just below the crest of the hill, there was a crew-size foxhole for a 60-mm mortar squad. Cottrell remembered the name of only one of the men, Douglas Lamp. But he remembered well the round that landed dead center in the hole. The vision of red blood midst the gray dust spurting forth like a fountain from the neck of one of the men was imprinted on his brain in permanent color. He felt sad that he could not remember the names of the other three men. He was not even sure how Lamp spelled his name, L-A-M-P or L-A-M-P-E. Somehow this did not seem right. The dead deserve more.

Cottrell felt somewhat secure in his own foxhole. An old tree trunk afforded partial overhead cover. But a mortar round slammed into it and shattered it to splinters. The tail fins of the round stuck in the dirt within inches of his head. He reached out to touch it, as if to be sure. It was still hot. He felt tremendous pressure in his head, especially his ears. He felt them with his hands. They came away sticky and red with blood. He felt woozy. Events seemed to be flowing before his eyes in slow motion. There was no medic around so he used the gauze in his first-aid pouch to stem the bleeding. The faintness faded. For the rest of the night he stayed at his post and aided the Third Squad in defending their share of the platoon front. At about daybreak he was evacuated with others on a half-track.

Not all the Chinese attackers that came along the ridge toward the second platoon could be seen by Chamberlin, or be fired upon by his machine-gun. Many of them were on the other side of the ridge and headed toward Sergeant McAfee's squad on the left.

The machine-gun attached to McAfee's squad did not work because of the dirt and debris of battle. Corporal Roland Lincke's BAR did not work either. Another battle casualty. But Private Herman Bilke had kept his M1 clean enough to work, except that it would not eject the shells and reload semiautomatically as it was supposed to.

So when about twenty-five Chinks came running toward them, Bilke lay on his back so he could kick the bolt back as Lincke shot over his prone body at the approaching enemy. As a team they operated the disabled M1 almost as fast as if it were working properly. But they were not fast enough to shoot all the Chinks. Some of them got very close, in hand grenade range. Lincke and Bilke used the last of their grenades to demolish the rest of the attackers. Then they withdrew into a tighter perimeter with their squad. They worked hard to clean their crippled weapons to be ready for the next wave of Chinese infantrymen.

Throughout the night Sergeant McAfee's squad held their positions. There was no communication with their platoon leader or the rest of the company. But they knew they were there, that they were not alone. They did not need to be told what to do. They had to fight or get killed. They could see the tracers from Chamberlin's machine-gun streaming across the ridge. They did not know who was firing the machine-gun, but they were glad to see the enemy drop.

There was no thought of bugging out. Private First Class Knox had warned them of the danger of that on Eerie. He was with them again tonight. He added his voice to Sergeant McAfee's orders to stay in their fox-holes and hold their positions. What less vocal men would have called shooting off your mouth too much in normal conditions, they now welcomed in the heat of battle. Unlike most boasters, Knox was not all mouth. He backed up his words by courage and action.

Finally, as dawn approached and the 2,000 rounds of machine-gun ammo at Chamberlin's gun were exhausted, the enemy withdrew. With them they carried most of their dead and wounded. They had tried at least three times to recapture Baldy that night, and each time they had failed. The second platoon had stood fast.

Chamberlin emerged from the foxhole and moved among the other foxholes to see about his men. His deep concern for their welfare was covered up by a cool casualness.

He came to where Browne was.

"Your men all right, Bob?"

"They're all alive, if that's what you mean. A few of them are wounded. I think my eardrums are busted."

"How about Jack?"

"He's okay. He did one hell of a job last night."

"Good." Chamberlin felt relieved.

Chamberlin saw two Chinks laying in a shell crater a few yards down the slope. One of them moved.

"I'm going to bayonet the bastards," he told Browne. "Cover me."

Chamberlin moved swiftly down the slope toward the prone men. Probably they were wounded, maybe even dead, he thought. But I'll stick 'em anyhow. If they're dead it won't hurt 'em. If they're not dead they might as well be. The thought of taking them prisoner never entered his mind. He wanted the feel of his bayonet plunging into human flesh.

Browne thought Chamberlin was crazy. As Chamberlin neared his goal, one of his intended victims rose up on one elbow. Chamberlin could have easily shot him. It was point-blank range. But his lust to bayonet was too great. From his higher vantage point Browne saw a grenade in the Chink's hand. He would have shot the enemy but his rifle was jammed. His only weapon was a grenade of his own.

"Watch out, Lieutenant!" he hollered, as he tossed the pear-shaped missile of death into the hole with the Chinks.

With the last of his energy the Chink heaved his grenade toward Chamberlin. It went about two feet and rolled back into the hole with its thrower.

Chamberlin saw the two grenades, and hit the dirt. He was so close the double blast seemed to lift him from the ground, but he was unhurt. He stood up and looked at the mutilated bodies. It did not seem to make sense to stick dead men now. At least, before, they might have been alive. Now there was no excuse. He walked back to Browne.

"What the hell did you do that for?" Chamberlin

99

asked Browne. "I wanted to stick the bastards with my bayonet."

"Yes, but one of them threw a grenade at you."

"Yeah, but shit, I would have got him."

But Chamberlin was not really angry at Browne. Their bond of protective courage allowed no real ire between them.

It now became fairly quiet on the battlefield. Chamberlain walked along the front to check his men. *How many were wounded? How many were dead?*

Miraculously, none of the Second Platoon were killed that night, and only eight were wounded seriously enough to be sent back for medical attention.

With the security of daylight, Chamberlin became very weary. He and the twelve men left in his platoon dozed in their holes on the battered dome of Baldy.

11

The sun did not rise on Baldy on 28 June 1952. The sky remained gray and ominous. Baldy was quiet now. The dead and wounded had been evacuated to the rear, to the graves registration unit or to hospital units as appropriate. Historical accounts were to record that six men were killed and sixty-one wounded in the night's battle. It also estimated the enemy casualties at 300, a ratio that military experts could brag about and make the hell of war more palatable to those removed from it.

Not long after daybreak, Lieutenant Moroney visited what was left of the Second Platoon. It was his mission to continue to hold Baldy. There had been no word from Battalion about relief. The number of casualties did not warrant it. Besides it was not expected that the Chinese would launch another attack soon. So Moroney would have to make do with what he had. Now he needed to check on the number of casualties the Second Platoon had suffered so he could evaluate its viability. Also, the figures were needed for the morning reports to be made out by administrative clerks in their well-protected bunkers in the rear. These figures were also important components of the military strategies proposed by the battle planners.

Moroney greeted Chamberlin warmly. "How you doing, Al?"

"Okay, I guess," Chamberlin answered wearily. "We

don't have many men left. Only twelve. I had to send Browne back. We don't have much ammo left. No food or water. My radioman was wounded and evacuated. We have no communications except the walkie-talkie, and that doesn't work too well."

"Okay, Al, I'll try to get some supplies to you. I'm trying to get Battalion to relieve us, but I don't know yet. Do you think you can hold out another night if they don't?"

"I don't know. We'll try. But we're spread pretty thin. My men are tired, thirsty, and hungry. I don't know how much more they can take."

Moroney returned to his CP. He reported his casualties to Battalion. His fears were confirmed. There would be no relief today. But supplies of ammo, water, and K rations were on their way.

Moroney weighed the factors. If the Chinese were to strike again, they would most likely use the same approach. Chamberlin's platoon was now at the lowest strength of his three rifle platoons. The Third Platoon was at the greatest strength and had seen the least action in the defenses of Eerie and Baldy. But he could depend on Chamberlin. He did not know about Lieutenant Fanjoy. He was untested. It was a tough decision. He called Fanjoy and Chamberlin and ordered them to switch positions.

The switch took place during midday with no hitch. Supplies were sent out as promised. The men were partially refreshed and rested. Rain started before dusk. Chamberlin set up his CP in a small foxhole with some overhead cover behind his platoon. It had been Fanjoy's the night before. Chamberlin had no CP to turn over to Fanjoy. Fanjoy wondered about Chamberlin's style of leadership, but he held his tongue. When his men were settled, he and his radioman dug their new CP on the reverse slope behind his men.

Neathery reported to Chamberlin that he had heard Chinese soldiers talking in some of the foxholes and caves in front of the positions where they were the night before—where the Third Platoon now was. He had heard them before they had left. He thought maybe they were sending messages back to their troops. He volunteered to blow them out with grenades. West offered to go with him. Chamberlin agreed it was the right thing to do.

Under cover of a smoke screen and near dusk, Neathery and West carried out their mission. There was no aggressive reaction from the Chinese in the holes. Probably they were mostly wounded and unarmed. But one could never tell for sure. It was safer to get rid of them. It was a risky task. Only a soldier like Neathery would think of it and offer to do it. Only a man like West would offer to help him.

Darkness shrouded Baldy again. The rain continued and intensified. The men were weary, wet, and cold. A few had ponchos, but not many. Some had overhead cover, but most did not. They had fought bravely the night before, but that did not decrease their fear.

Chamberlin sat on an empty ammunition box in his CP. He dozed as much as he could. This served a double function. It gave his body a chance to recuperate and deluded him about the passage of time. As long as he could sleep he knew the Chinese were not coming.

But nobody rested for long that night on Baldy. As if embarrassed by their defeat the night before, the Chinese decided to save face by doing tonight what they had not been able to do the night before. It started out as a repetition of the previous night. Artillery and mortars dueled again. But this time the Chinese used two battalions of infantry instead of one. They attacked from both the left and right, hitting the Third and First platoons.

Chamberlin huddled in his foxhole with the radio in his hand. He could hear random conversations among Moroney and his other platoon leaders, so he was able to keep abreast of the situation from his CP. He rationalized that it was important for him to know what was going on and that it was easier to do this inside the CP than outside with his men. In the CP the din of battle was dampened somewhat by the overhead cover.

Even in the midst of the shelling he dozed off occasionally—whether from weariness or an unconscious attempt to escape the horror of reality—who knows? In any case, sleep was not very successful. He became very depressed and frightened. He felt trapped. Combat was a confused mess of entanglements. It made no sense. There was no logic to it. It was dirty, untidy, and above all, painful. A thought kept going through his head. *If I ever get through this fucking mess, nothing will ever faze me. I'll be able to do anything.*

The Chinese forces assaulted the Third Platoon under cover of darkness. Flares lit the battlefield too late. Chinese and Americans intermingled and fought hand-to-hand. Lieutenant Fanjoy was bayoneted in the genital area and left for dead in the bottom of his foxhole. His platoon positions were completely overrun.

On the right flank of L Company, another Chinese battalion hit the First Platoon area. Here, too, they were successful in overrunning the defensive positions. Early on in the shelling, several rounds tore up the soil around Sergeant Bill Browne's foxhole. Flying shrapnel slashed at his face and arms. An armored vest protected his torso. The disturbed dirt was redeposited around, on and over Browne's mutilated body. He was completely buried. Whether from the wounds and subsequent loss of blood, concussion, shock or lack of air, he lapsed into unconsciousness.

Perhaps the rim of his helmet formed a small air pocket or the angle of his neck bent forward. Perhaps the steady rain forced an airway through the sand. Whatever it was, he survived dormantly buried for a long time. Perhaps even, his unrequested burial protected him from a worse fate. While buried he was not a target for the enemy as they roamed the battle arena in search of American prey. He was hidden from their view. His cover also afforded him some protection from artillery fire.

As the night passed and the battle continued to rage around him, the steady downpour gradually washed away the debris covering his helmet. A rescue squad spotted him, dug him out, and evacuated him back through the medical pipeline to safety.

The Chinese were now running all around the top of Baldy. They reached the edges of the Second Platoon area. One ran up to the foxhole occupied by Partin and Kentucky. Kentucky was on duty, as they would say, taking care of Partin. The Chink had a grenade. Why? Who knows? Who can explain the lunacy of war? But he used the grenade like a club and hit Partin in the face with it. It took a big chip out of one of Partin's upper front teeth. Then the Chink turned and ran. Kentucky told Partin to hold still. He rested his M1 on Partin's shoulder and shot the retreating Chink. The grenade fell silently to the bottom of their foxhole. It did not explode. The stupid Chink had forgotten to pull the pin. Neither Partin nor Kentucky noticed it until after Kentucky had shot its deliverer. Partin kept it as a souvenir and evidence in the tale of his chipped tooth.

Another Chink ran up behind West's position. West

did not see him. He was busy firing at foes in front of him. From a nearby foxhole, Knox saw the Chink about to bayonet West. Somewhere in the confusion of battle, Knox had latched onto a Colt .45, one of the most prized of war mementos. He used it now. The .45 slug scattered Chinese brains on the battlefield. It also locked Knox to West in an everlasting bond of courage.

When Moroney realized that the Third Platoon was being overrun, he called Chamberlin on the walkie-talkie. He wanted Chamberlin to lead his platoon in a counterattack. He tried to say as much on the radio. But Chamberlin, even though he had a pretty good idea what Moroney wanted, could not understand him. Moroney was so excited that his words did not come out right.

"Mike, calm down," Chamberlin said in a low, deceptively cool voice. "I can't understand you. Get the shit out of your mouth."

Finally Moroney was able to tell Chamberlin to meet him out behind his CP, several yards to the left of Chamberlin's CP.

Chamberlin grabbed his carbine and went out to meet Moroney. The battlefield was now dimly lit by flares. The shelling had slackened. As they were talking above the din of small arms fire, a shadowy figure ran toward them. His unhelmeted profile attested to his hostile identity. Chamberlin moved a little apart from Moroney to divide the attention of their foe. The Chink tossed a grenade at them. But, as if the thrower were confused as to which body to target, it landed midway between them and exploded harmlessly. Chamberlin fired his carbine at the retreating grenadier. It was difficult to aim in the dim light and he was not sure he hit him. Not that it mattered much at this point. He returned to Moroney to see what he wanted.

A well-rested, well-fed, dry, warm staff officer fielded his message.

"Lieutenant, you must hold Baldy at all costs. Do you want hot food sent out?"

"My men are wet and cold. We need blankets more than anything else,"" replied Moroney.

"Do you want the hot food or not," snapped the staff officer.

"Yes, but please send us some blankets," pleaded Moroney.

The staff officer discontinued the conversation in a cold, professional, military manner.

The hot food was brought out along with more ammunition. But there were no blankets. Perhaps they could not be wasted.

Like all good times, bad times also eventually must cease, except for those who are crippled for life. Even for those, death comes finally. A quick end is only for the lucky.

L Company was finally relieved late in the day on 29 June 1952. A weary, ragged crew, they slowly filed off the southern slope of Baldy and took refuge and rest in some bunkers on the MLR. The men were fed and they rested. Chamberlin slept the night through. In the morning Moroney woke him.

"Wake up, Al. It's time for breakfast and then we're moving back," he said.

"Do I have to get up, Mike?" asked a sleepy Chamberlin.

"Here's some breakfast," said Moroney as he handed Chamberlin a mess kit full of pancakes.

Chamberlin woke long enough to gulp down the pancakes and a second helping, along with a canteen cup full of hot coffee. Then he collapsed back into sleep.

"Let him sleep," Moroney said to those around him. "He has earned a rest. He can catch up with us when he wakes up."

So, when what was left of L Company moved back to the same reserve position they had occupied when Chamberlin first joined them, Chamberlin slept on in the bunker on the MLR.

12

Sergeant Bob Browne moved back through the medical pipeline to a MASH unit somewhere east of Seoul. His head was splitting with pain. He was given aspirin and the pain slackened somewhat. He was examined several times and placed in a ward for five days of observation. He wondered why. Did they think he was faking it? Sure, he had been scared. But only fools were not scared. He was no fool and for damn sure he was no coward. Maybe he should have stayed with his men. Maybe he was not hurt as badly as he thought.

As he lay on a bunk in the medical tent on the night of 28 June, a nearby radio was blaring out news from the front. It reported that Baldy was being hit the second night in a row and casualties were heavy. He thought of his men. Did they need him? Would they think he had deserted them? Would Chamberlin lose his respect for him? But mostly he thought of his brother, Bill. He should be there to take care of him. He never dreamed the Chinks would attack in such force two nights in a row.

No one was paying him much mind. They were all too busy getting ready for the expected influx of casualties from the night's fighting. He grabbed his stuff and left the tent. He did not know where he was, but he knew Baldy was north. He flagged down a jeep and hitched a ride northward. Other rides eventually brought him to the MLR behind Baldy. But by then it was daylight and the night's battle for Baldy was over. Even if he had been allowed, it no longer made sense to go on out to Baldy. What could he do now? And his head was aching again. He was sure that L Company would be relieved after two nights in a row of heavy fighting. So he waited on the MLR, a guest of another company. He got some more aspirin for his headache.

Little did he know that as he traveled north, his unconscious brother was journeying south. Perhaps their vehicles passed in the night. It was the end of the war for Bill. Now he would start his own personal battle of healing, recuperation, and rehabilitation. For him, Fanjoy, Porter, and many others, this would be a longer battle than the bout for Baldy, and would often require equal or even greater courage to win.

Sergeant Bob Browne was reunited with L Company when they left the MLR on the morning of 30 June 1952 and returned to their blocking position in the rear. The initial report that his brother had been hit badly and possibly had not made it left him frantic. It renewed his guilt. Why had he not been there? But later news revealed that Bill was alive. This was a relief. At least now there was hope. Visions of a crippled brother were more pleasant than of a dead one. He wondered where they would have had the funeral.

His squad welcomed Bob Browne warmly. When he had left Baldy, he had entrusted Neathery with his M1 rifle because Neathery had broken his against a hardheaded Chink. Browne thought a lot of his piece and had always kept it in good shape. It had been zeroed in just the way he wanted it. Now he wanted it back.

"Where's my rifle?" he asked Neathery after the initial greetings.

"Boy, am I glad to see you back," replied Neathery. "We thought that maybe you were really wounded."

"Don't change the subject," ordered Browne, his voice low, slow, and serious. "Where's my M1?"

"Did they give you a Purple Heart?" quipped Neathery.

"Of course they gave me a Purple Heart. Everybody that's wounded gets a Purple Heart. But don't change the subject. Where's my damn rifle?"

Neathery did not know how to evade the issue any longer. "Well, Bob, the next night the Chinks came back and we had to fight some more. I ran out of ammo and I slung it at one of them. Then I couldn't find it."

Browne was disappointed at the loss of his rifle because of the special affection he had had for it. But all was not lost. He had recovered one of the Russian-made rifles a Chinaman had tried to do him in with. They were not supposed to keep such weapons as souvenirs, but he would figure out how to get it home some way. He was also very thankful that all of his men were still alive.

"My head is killing me," said Browne. "I wish I had a beer."

"I don't think there's any beer around," answered Neathery. "But Partin and Kentucky have been acting like they don't feel no pain. Maybe they've got something."

"Let's find out," said Browne. "I'll pull rank on them."

Browne and Neathery proceeded to the pup tent shared by Partin and Kentucky.

"I heard you've been drinking," said Browne with squad leader seriousness. "You know that's not allowed on the front lines."

"Oh no," lied Kentucky with a sober face. "We don't

drink no more. Not after what we went through on Baldy. We saw the light."

"Yeah," chimed in Partin. "We got religion that first night. We asked the Lord to save us and He did. So we promised to never drink no more. Do you guys have to fight like that very often?"

"Oh that's just routine," said Neathery. "We usually pull that kind of detail every week or so."

"Damn it, let's stick to the point," said Browne. "I want to check your duffle bags."

"Okay," agreed Kentucky. "We've had a little bit to drink. Don't tell anybody and we'll let you have some."

Between the two of them they had ten bottles of whiskey.

"Where did you get all this?" demanded Browne.

"You'd better let me tell 'em," Partin said to Kentucky. "You're too dumb."

Then to Browne he explained, "You see, Kentucky don't get paid much. Only twenty dollars a month. The rest he sends to his mother. Well, the Army screwed up and didn't pay him for over ten months. Then when he got paid he bought whiskey in the black market down in Pusan."

"What did he do for money all that time?" asked Browne.

"Well, I had to take care of him," said Partin, "I promised his mother I would. Now he's going to pay me back. Half the whiskey is mine."

They all had a drink. Browne's headache eased and he went to supply and got another M1. Everybody knew that nobody was really angry at anybody.

During the day L Company had a surprise visitor, General "Bulldog" Smith. He wanted to meet some living examples of the 45th Division's fighting men.

Moroney assembled the company for the general's inspection.

"Where are the rest of your men?" asked the general.

"These are all I have left, Sir," replied Moroney.

"Where are the rest of your officers?" Smith continued to question.

Moroney was embarrassed. He wished he had made Chamberlin get up that morning and stay with the company. "I have only one left, Sir."

"Where the hell is he? Why isn't he here? I want to see him. What's his name?" demanded the general.

As a lawyer, Moroney was quick of tongue, but he could think of no excuse better than the truth. "His name is Lieutenant Chamberlin, Sir. We left him on the MLR this morning. He was still asleep when we left. He'll join us when he wakes up."

Smith had never encountered such a situation. He was mad as hell. "Dismiss your men, Lieutenant," he ordered. "I want to talk to you in private in your CP."

"Dismissed," Moroney ordered his men. He led Smith to his CP.

The men grumbled as they fell out. They thought Moroney and Chamberlin were in trouble. Who the hell did the general think he was? What did he know about combat? All he ever did was sit on his fat ass in the rear echelon and ride around in his whirlybird. They were pissed off.

Smith asked Moroney, "Why did you let Lieutenant Chamberlin sleep this morning?"

Moroney answered simply, "Because he had fought hard for two nights in a row and was exhausted, Sir. I didn't think I would need him today."

"What about the other men?" questioned Smith.

"Oh, they didn't mind." Moroney deliberately put his own twist on the question. "We all have great respect for him."

Smith softened. Seldom in his long military career had he witnessed a soldier's personal concern for another soldier. His army had not allowed for personal attachments. One did things by the book and as ordered. There was no room for subjective sentiment. But now he was moved by Moroney's softheartedness.

"Is he a good combat leader?" asked Smith.

"He's the best," Moroney replied. "I recommended him for a Silver Star for his action on Eerie and I'm going to put him in for another medal for what he did on Baldy."

"What did he do on Baldy?" asked Smith.

"Well, I don't have all the details yet," answered Moroney. "I've got to talk to some of his men. But I heard he fires a mean machine-gun."

"Lieutenant, you and your men did a good job holding Baldy," said Smith. "That's a good thing you're doing, I believe the men should get all the medals and promotions they deserve. Good for morale. By the way, what's Chamberlin's rank?"

"Second Lieutenant, Sir," responded Moroney. "He's only been with us about a month."

"Does he deserve to be promoted?" asked Smith.

"He sure as hell does," Moroney replied exuberantly.

Smith turned to his aide. "Have Lieutenant Chamberlin promoted by special order today."

Chamberlin woke later in the day. The events of the past twenty-four hours were vague to him. It took a moment for him to realize where he was. Then he gathered his things together, buckled on his cartridge belt, tied the thongs around his thighs and moved out of the bunker. Soon he found someone and arranged a ride back to his company.

As soon as he arrived, Moroney ordered the company to assemble. He ordered Chamberlin front and center. Chamberlin wondered what in hell was going on. Was he going to get chewed out?

Chamberlin stood in front of Moroney. He was dirty and unshaven. His fatigues were dirty, sweaty and smelled. Sweat rings darkened his jacket under the arm pits. He could just as well have stepped out of a Bill Maudlin cartoon.

Moroney stepped forward. He unpinned the silver bar from his own collar and pinned it on Chamberlin's collar.

"Sorry," he said. "This is the only first lieutenant's bar in the company. You are now a first lieutenant. General Smith was here today and promoted you."

For a moment Chamberlin was speechless. He did not know what to say or do. He felt uncomfortable. Moroney helped him by grasping his hand with a strong, warm grip.

"Thanks, Mike," Chamberlin said simply.

The next day Chamberlin again got together with his squad leaders. He was technically the company executive officer now, but that had not really sunk in yet. He still felt like the Second Platoon leader. He talked with them about the battles on Baldy and it was decided who had earned awards and who would write statements about whom. He recommended Browne and Neathery for Distinguished Service Crosses. Others were recommended for Silver or Bronze Stars. Notable exceptions again were Sergeants Sides and Amos. Johnson was also excluded because of his lack of courage. Chamberlin thought about putting Sides in for the Bronze Star. He had finally got up enough nerve to fire his rifle a few times at the enemy, but only after much urging. No, he did not really think Sides deserved any award. As far as anyone knew, Amos had again been invisible on the battlefield.

Also there were many promotions recommended due to the high casualty rate. The company clerk was swamped with paperwork. Priorities had to be established. The daily administrative stuff had to be done. Promotions were next. Soldiers needed all the money they could get. They also needed the authority to go with added responsibility. Schiefer had his work cut out for him. While he worked long hours organizing, typing, and filing, the men relaxed and rested. Schiefer envied them. They got all the promotions, all the glory, all the rest. His job was never done.

A few days after Baldy, good news came for Lieutenant Moroney: rotation back to the States. He turned the company over to Chamberlin. As he left, he unhooked his Colt .45 from his cartridge belt and handed it to Chamberlin.

"Al, I give you as a final token of my deep respect and appreciation for what you've done," he said.

"Thank you very much, Mike," replied Chamberlin. "That means a lot coming from you."

The fact that it was a government-issue Colt .45 was immaterial to Chamberlin. To him it was a personal gift from one warrior to another. He accepted it as his own, not as a piece of government equipment. He had to make some minor adjustments to the other pieces of his arsenal to make room for it on his cartridge belt. And it added another thong to be tied around his right thigh.

Somewhere along the line he had also added a grenade pouch on the left front of his belt, with a four-grenade capacity and more thongs around his left thigh.

Patton had had his pearl-handled pistols in World War II. Ridgeway had grenades decorating his suspenders. Now Chamberlin had his own persona. One difference: his was more functional than fancy.

The men of L Company were sorry to see Moroney go. He had been good to them, as had been Lieutenant Pierce before him. He had treated them with respect, dignity, and consideration. They were also happy for him. Now they were glad that Chamberlin would be their commanding officer, or so they thought.

Those thoughts were soon put to rest, however. The very next day Captain Brown arrived to take over the company.

13

Captain Brown ordered that the company be assembled. He wanted to talk to his men. The men were not happy that Lieutenant Moroney was being replaced by a newcomer, rather than Lieutenant Chamberlin. But they had no choice. Whatever the Army is, it is not a democracy.

Captain Brown was a small man, perhaps five foot six, weighing about 130 pounds. His fatigues were spotless and well-starched. His combat boots glistened, as did his captain's bars. He was a sharp contrast to what the company had come to expect of their officers. They were used to strong leaders—if not dirty, at least soiled and rumpled by the rigors of war. All that Chamberlin had known had been young. Brown appeared to be at least thirty.

Captain Brown told the men about himself. How he had been to Officers Candidate School during World War II. About his military assignments, including a stint as a general's aide, about his family, his education, and other stuff, as if the men cared. Chamberlin wondered how the hell a man, who was older than he was could have been in the Army during World War II, staying in since then, and never been overseas before this. His speech also included what he expected of the men—the usual garrison-type chickenshit: shave every day, police up their area, keep weapons clean, shine their boots, and follow orders when he led them into battle, which he hoped to do soon.

This made the men mad. They did not want to be led into battle again by anyone, much less a greenhorn. Most of them were short-timers, near rotation, and did not want to take any more chances. Nor did they like chick-enshit.

After Captain Brown retreated to his CP the men spoke up to Chamberlin.

Sergeant Sides, who was now the company first sergeant due to the rotation of his predecessor, said, "Lieutenant, you better talk to him. None of us want to go back into battle."

"Yeah," spoke up Bob Browne, who had taken over Sides's job as platoon sergeant of the Second Platoon. "You better straighten him out. We've been through enough already. We don't want some damn greenhorn volunteering us for combat missions. Why the hell didn't they let you be our company commander? You know what's going on."

"Yeah, if he thinks I'm going to shine my fucking boots, he's got another think coming," chimed in Sergeant Davidson of the Third Platoon. "He can kiss my ass."

There was a rumble of general agreement amid the ranks of the ragged-looking men.

Chamberlin stood before them and held up his hand for their attention.

"Let's wait and see what happens," he said softly. "Captain Brown is new and doesn't understand what you men have gone through. But we have to give him a chance. Maybe he'll turn out okay. In the meantime, I will be talking to him."

Captain Brown was impressed with Chamberlin. He had sensed the men's mutinous mood as he left. Then he had noted Chamberlin's easy control of them, even though he could not hear his words from where he stood inside his tent flap. He longed for that kind of control. Chamberlin was a good man to have around, he thought. He could use him.

One day Captain Brown, Chamberlin, and a few others were just hanging around shooting the bull. Brown wanted to talk about combat. He had heard a lot of discussions about the fighting the men had been in, especially in his conversations with his first sergeant, Sides, and the company clerk, Schiefer. He now wanted very much to be part of this inner circle of courageous men. Chamberlin and the others, however, did not want to let him in, any more than any other unproven person. They only tolerated his presence because he was their commanding officer.

"I'm a pretty good shot," bragged Brown. "I shot 'expert' with all weapons in OCS. How'd you do, Chamberlin?"

"Oh, I qualified okay," answered Chamberlin reluctantly. "But I didn't go to OCS. I took ROTC in college."

"I bet I'm a better shot than you are," challenged Brown. "When we go back on the line we can have a contest. I bet I can shoot more Chinks than you can. Ten bucks says I can."

"Oh, I wouldn't be surprised," agreed Chamberlin. "But I really wouldn't want to compete with you. Combat is no game."

"I hear it was as easy as shooting ducks on a pond," argued Brown. "I can't wait to pick off a few."

A few days later, Captain Brown's chance of becoming a great combat hero started approaching fruition. L Company was ordered back up on the MLR.

Captain Brown sat at his field desk and labored hard over his first combat order. He checked it against his trusted field manual to be sure he had covered everything. Then he called Chamberlin in and asked him his opinion.

Chamberlin remembered vaguely what the manual said about field orders and what he had learned in Infantry School. But Lieutenants Pierce and Moroney had always been more concerned with what had to be done than how well their orders were written. He had never known them to read orders to their men. He glanced at Brown's work briefly.

"Everything seems to be covered," he said.

What to Captain Brown was a big deal was nothing to Chamberlin. They had made this move several times already and all the men knew what to do, field order or no field order.

Captain Brown called the platoon sergeants, mess sergeant, and supply sergeant together and read them his carefully prepared field order. Now that he was actually about to embark on his combat career, he seemed much less exuberant about it than before, when it had only been a dream. His demeanor spoke of his hidden fears. He appeared timid, meek, and above all, small and weak.

But there was no problem. The men, their equipment, and gear were transported up to the MLR as they had been many times before. Captain Brown seemed almost a nonentity in the process.

Soon Captain Brown's true colors began to emerge. It was a hot, humid day. Communications Sergeant Spisak reported to him in his CP. Spisak was not wearing a fatigue jacket. His white T-shirt was far from white. His face looked unwashed. His blond, curly hair was rumpled and uncombed because he had just removed his steel helmet.

"How dare you come into my presence like that?"

the captain yelled. "Where's your fatigue jacket? Go back to your quarters and clean up. Don't ever come into my CP again out of uniform."

"But, Sir, I just wanted to tell you—" the dumfounded Spisak started to say.

"Get out!" ordered the captain.

Spisak left.

Chamberlin, who had been listening with surprise at Brown's insistence on military protocol, followed him out.

"Sergeant, what was it you wanted to tell Captain Brown?" he asked, thinking it might be important.

"I just wanted to warn him that Battalion called and said there was going to be some staff officers coming up to inspect our positions," Spisak said.

"I'll tell him," offered Chamberlin. "Try not to worry too much about Captain Brown. Maybe he'll learn."

As Captain Brown, Chamberlin, Sergeant Sides, and the officers from Battalion toured the positions a little later, a random mortar round landed about a hundred yards away, well out of the zone of concern. Captain Brown ducked and cowered behind a small bush. None of the others even flinched. Not even Sides. They looked at Brown and wondered.

Remember Private White, the black lad that had chickened out when the company first went out on Baldy? After he was reunited with the company, he was completely ostracized by the rest of the men. Even his buddy, Johnson, refused to share a pup tent with him or speak to him. Finally, when he could no longer stand the isolation and rejection, he pleaded with Lieutenant Chamberlin for an audience.

Chamberlin felt sorry for White, but did not want to

condone his cowardice. Nor did he want to press charges against him. What good would come of it? There was no danger that any of his men would succumb to his bad example. Besides, he was influenced by his own court-martial in World War II when he had told his first ser-geant, a guy by the name of Tremont, to go fuck himself. The thirty days of hard labor and two-thirds pay cut had not done him any good.

"What do you want?" Chamberlin asked.

"Lieutenant, the men all hate me. I can't stand it. Please give me another chance," begged White.

"Okay, I'll give you another chance," agreed Chamberlin. "When we go back up on the line, I'll treat you just like anybody else. But I can't stop the men from hating you. You have to prove yourself."

Baldy had now been secure for some time. Foxholes and gun positions were now well fortified with overhead cover and sandbags. The Chinese had given up trying to take it back.

L Company was ordered to relieve the outfit that now occupied it. Chamberlin took the second platoon and a few men from each of the decimated First and Third Platoons out to man the positions on Baldy. Captain Brown would have liked to stay on the relatively safe MLR. But he had no choice. Orders called for him to occupy a CP on a small knoll between Baldy and the MLR. With him were Sergeants Sides, Spisak, and a few other headquarters personnel.

Chamberlin and Sergeant Browne set up their CP on the reverse slope of Baldy. Occasional artillery rounds and small-arms fire broke up the boredom as time passed. Nothing significant happened, except once enemy mortars tried to bracket in on Captain Brown's CP.

Sergeant Browne answered the phone in Chamberlin's CP. It was Sergeant Sides.

"Bob, I need help," Sides cried frantically. "Captain Brown is going crazy. He's hiding in a corner with a blanket over his head. He wants us to fill sandbags and build a wall to protect him. I don't know what the hell to do. He's driving me crazy. Ask Chamberlin what I should do."

Sergeant Browne laughed as he relayed the message to Chamberlin.

Chamberlin grinned. "Tell him to come on up and we'll have our shooting contest. It's not dangerous out here."

When Sides heard that he said, "He can't do that. He's scared shitless. He's driving me nuts. I wish I were out there with you guys."

Browne told Sides, "Tell him not to worry. There's no danger unless they score a direct hit. And even then his blanket might save him."

Hot meals were brought out to the men on Baldy by Korean chogie crews. The men would leave a couple of guys in a gun position on the forward slope while the rest went back to the reverse slope to eat. At a noon meal, Privates Mason Bowman and LeRoy White were on guard. Suddenly White came running down the reverse slope yelling, "He's dead! He's dead!"

Neathery and West grabbed their rifles and ran to check on Bowman. White was right. He was dead. A direct-fire weapon had scored a bull's-eye through the gun's firing aperture. The concussion had killed Bowman. Blood was slowly oozing from his ears, mouth, nose and eyes. It was like all the blood cells in his brain had burst. White was unhurt.

West reported the death to Chamberlin. Chamberlin looked at Browne. There was pain in his eyes. He did not want to see a dead Bowman. He had held him in his arms before. He was not sure how he would react faced with the dead body of one of his men. He had not seen Dawes after he was dead. He did not want to break down and lose control in front of his men.

"Bob, would you take care of his things?" Chamberlin asked.

"Sure," said Browne. He thought he understood Chamberlin's unexpressed feelings.

Chamberlin sat by himself for awhile trying to block out the reality of death. He knew Bowman was married and had some kids. He liked to show pictures of them to his buddies. All the men liked Bowman.

Later Neathery said, "Frenchy knew he was going to get killed. He didn't want to go back on Baldy for that reason. He told me and Bill that he had a dream and saw his dead body. Boy, he had guts. He was a hell of a good man."

Orders came down that the 45th Division was moving over to the east central front. L Company was to be relieved on Baldy. While the main forces were being relieved on the MLR under cover of darkness, Chamberlin had to set up a listening post out in the valley to the left of Baldy to prevent any sneak attacks. This was done with no problem.

Captain Brown and the rest of the company moved off the line, packed up the company gear, loaded onto a convoy of trucks and moved out.

As dawn broke Chamberlin brought his patrol back to the MLR and on down the slopes to where they were to be picked up by transportation.

At the foot of the hill Colonel Spottswood waited in

a jeep to be sure all his men were accounted for. Chamberlin spotted him and moved apart from his men to report to him.

"Mission accomplished, Sir," he said as he saluted.

Spottswood returned his salute. "Were there any problems, Lieutenant?" he asked.

"No problems, Sir," said Chamberlin.

"Job well done, Chamberlin," said Spottswood. "I knew we could count on you."

"Thank you, Sir," said Chamberlin.

The men loaded onto a truck and they moved out. They were glad to be leaving. Nothing could be worse than Baldy, Eerie and Porkchop. They were very weary of war. They closed their eyes and rested as the truck rolled along the dusty road.

14

When L Company arrived at their new destination it was already dark. It was raining very hard. The men are cold and tired from the long trip. They hoped that now they could rest.

But there was work to be done first. The mess tent, supply tent, and headquarters tent had to be set up. All the equipment from each of these units had to be unloaded and organized. Only then could they concern themselves with their own individual duffle bags, pitch their pup tents, and finally make their beds on the muddy ground.

The equipment from the headquarters unit was unloaded onto the mud. All kinds of field office supplies—typewriter, files, papers, odds and ends, were moved out from under the protection of the truck tarpaulin into the rain and mud. Nothing had been well-packed or organized. The trucks had to get back to the motor pool. Captain Brown was fit to be tied, but seemed helpless and ignorant of what to do.

Chamberlin was not sure what to do either, or even who was responsible to do what. He had not been briefed, and this was an entirely new situation for him. But it was not a life-or-death deal, so he was not about to waste any adrenaline on it.

There was very little light to work with—only the headlights from the few company vehicles and a few random flashlights. So Chamberlin suggested they cover the office equipment with a tarpaulin and let the men find their duffle bags, pitch their pup tents and get some rest. Then when it was daylight, they could put up the headquarters tent and organize things. Brown did not give a shit about the men resting or taking care of their own personal needs. He wanted the headquarters tent set up immediately and all the office supplies out of the mud and rain.

This was perhaps the first time that the priorities of Brown and Chamberlin clashed. Actually it was the first time they had to do anything together.

Chamberlin won out not so much because of strength of will, but because there were not enough men available to put up the headquarters tent. The mess and supply sergeants had commandeered the men before Brown could get unraveled. And Sergeant Sides was no help to him. He had little or no control over the men. It was as if their performance in combat correlated with their ability to command. The men did not want to be told what to do by cowards.

But they got through the night somehow. In the next few days tents were pitched and equipment was organized. Chamberlin's main concern was the morale and well-being of the men. The men's main concern, since there were no women around, seemed to be to drink beer. There was not much of that around either. And what there was, was soon gone.

Chamberlin and Sergeant Browne decided that they could probably get some beer if they went back to a quartermaster outfit in Chunchon, about sixty miles south. Chamberlin approached Captain Brown.

"Captain Brown, the men are pretty restless and their morale is low," he said. "I think if they had some beer they would feel better. Sergeant Browne knows somebody back in quartermaster and thinks he can get us some beer. If we could use the company jeep for a few hours, I'd be glad to go with him and see if we can get some beer for the men."

Captain Brown hesitated for a moment. But he was not yet ready to try to buck Chamberlin. "Okay," he agreed.

So Sergeant Browne, Chamberlin, Neathery, and a driver hooked a trailer on the jeep and went to get beer. On the way south they passed through a military police checkpoint. Chamberlin dismounted from the jeep at their request. The two young MPs took a quick look at his .45 Colt, twin daggers, and grenades all tied down securely with thongs around his thighs. They saluted stiffly and told him to pass on.

"Lieutenant, those guys acted like they know you," said the driver, Private Oswald.

"Maybe they do," agreed Browne.

"They probably don't know our names, but they know we're combat men," said Neathery. "You can always tell a combat man when you see one."

Chamberlin thought about what Neathery said. There did seem to be an unspoken recognition and reverence for combat veterans, phenomena not just found in noncombatants, but among battle-hardened warriors as well. Neathery was wise far beyond his education and age.

They drove on to Chunchon.

"How would you guys like to get laid before we go back?" asked Chamberlin.

"Yeah, I would," said Oswald. He was a new replacement and had not yet been in combat. Getting laid with some combat men seemed like the manly thing to do. Very exciting.

"Not me," said Browne. "All I want is some beer."

"Why don't you drop Bob and me off at quartermaster?" said Neathery. "We can get the beer while you and Oswald go get laid."

"Good, then we'll pick you guys up later," said Chamberlin.

And so it happened. Browne and Neathery negotiated for beer at quartermaster while Chamberlin and Oswald found a whorehouse. Neither was difficult. The noncommissioned officers club where Browne and Neathery went to get the beer welcomed them warmly. They were eager to hear combat tales from the lips of heroes such as Browne and Neathery. They gave them as much beer as they wanted. The town was loaded with houses that made their living catering to the lust of U.S. GIs. Chamberlin and Oswald soon found a vent for their needs.

As Chamberlin lay with his woman, he suddenly felt very guilty. Here he was enjoying himself while his men were up there suffering in that hellhole. When he was finished he asked the mamasan if she had any girls who wanted to make a lot of money by going up to service his men. She found two girls that were excited at the prospect of earning big bucks.

Chamberlin and Oswald took the two girls, picked up Browne and Neathery and a trailer full of beer and headed back to camp.

"What the hell are we going to do when we get to the MP checkpoint?" asked Browne.

"We'll bluff our way through," laughed a happy Neathery. "If that don't work, Oswald, just step on the gas and go like hell."

They put field jackets on the girls. Then Browne and Neathery separated their steel helmets from their helmet liners and put the steel helmets on the girls. The girls giggled. They squeezed down in the narrow back set of the jeep while Browne and Neathery sat up tall on the wheel housings.

When they reached the check point it was dark. The MPs stopped them as it was their duty. But they did not want to deal with any complications.

Chamberlin returned their salute without getting out of the jeep. "I'm Lieutenant Chamberlin from the 45th Infantry," he said.

"Who are your passengers?" one of the MPs inquired.

"Oh them," replied Chamberlin as he stalled for time and ideas. "We're not supposed to tell anybody, but since you're doing such a good job and have caught us, we'll have to share this Top Secret counterintelligence information with you. We're part of operation 'Pussy Cat.' They're Korean moles from Division Intelligence. We have to escort them up to the MLR so they can infiltrate the enemy positions. Remember, this is top secret so General Ruffner doesn't want anybody to know about it. So my orders to you from the general are to keep your eyes open and your mouths shut. I will personally let the General know what a good job you guys are doing."

"Yes, Sir," said the MP.

"We're going to be returning through this check point in a few hours with some returning moles, so pass the word on to your relief," continued Chamberlin.

"Yes, Sir," said the MP. "Pass on." *Boy, what a story he would have to tell his friends and folks back home! He actually was taking part in a combat intelligence operation!*

Chamberlin's escort service moved on up the road.

They laughed like hell about their "Pussy Cat" operation.

They moved into camp silently and set up two pup tents for the girls' privacy. Then they spread the word to the second platoon. They planned to keep it a small operation just among friends. But word spread rapidly. Soon customers were coming from the whole company and lines were forming at the pup tents.

As Chamberlin was letting some of the men know about the girls, he passed Sergeant Sides's bunk. Sides was sound asleep lying on his back with a big hard-on making a tent out of his blanket. Chamberlin wanted to wake him without making a lot of noise, so he snapped his genital tent pole gently with his index finger.

"Jim," he whispered. "You want a piece of ass?"

"What the hell you talking about?" a startled Sides said. "Are you drunk?"

"Come on," Chamberlin whispered. "I'll show you."

Whether he went or not Sides would never say.

Business was so heavy that Chamberlin decided to handle the money himself. He did not want the girls to get cheated. It was two bucks a piece. Jack Tally, who had done some pimping back home in Kentucky, wanted a little extra time. It took him longer he said. And he knew that time was money for the girls, so his sense of honor made him offer five dollars for his turn.

As word spread, men from nearby K and M Companies started queuing up among the L Company men. Chamberlin became worried that they would get caught, but they did not. Much as the battles on Eerie and Baldy had petered out toward dawn, this business also tapered off in the wee hours of the morning.

Chamberlin gathered up his crew and the girls and they retraced their route back to their homes in

Chunchon. There were no questions asked at the check point. Mamasan and the two girls shared over $200 in military scrip equal to 3,000 yen—a small fortune to them. Chamberlin kept nothing for his services.

After Chamberlin and his men returned to camp and he had slept most of the day, Captain Brown approached him, tentatively.

"Al, what's this I hear about there being some girls in camp last night?" he asked.

"Captain, I don't know anything about it," Chamberlin lied. "But I'll take full responsibility."

Captain Brown did not know how to handle such an ambiguous answer. He had no concrete facts to go on so he did not pursue the issue. Besides, he was beginning to sense a hostility toward him from Chamberlin and this scared him.

Most of the men enjoyed the beer brought back from quartermaster. Many got very drunk. Kentucky got so drunk that he decided it was time to do away with Captain Brown. He took a loaded .45 Colt and was about to head for the company CP. Browne, Neathery, and West held him back but could not get him to give up the .45. Chamberlin's presence was requested.

"How you doing, Kentucky?" asked Chamberlin.

"I'm drunker'n a piss pot," said Kentucky. "I'm going to blow Captain Brown's fucking head off."

"I don't blame you, but I don't want you to do that," said Chamberlin.

"Nobody can stop me. I've got the gun," said Kentucky.

"What about your mother?" asked Chamberlin. "Who's going to take care of her if you shoot Captain Brown and end up in the stockade?"

"She gets an allotment from my pay," said Kentucky. "That takes care care of her."

"But Kentucky, you won't get any pay in the stockade and your mother won't get any allotment," said Chamberlin. "Didn't you know that?"

"Nobody told me that," said Kentucky. "Hey Partin, you son-of-a-bitch, how come you never told me that? You're supposed to take care of me."

Partin, who had been torn between protecting Captain Brown from Kentucky and protecting Kentucky from Browne, Neathery, and West, retorted, "You're too dumb to listen."

Chamberlin sat down on the bunk beside Kentucky and put his arm around his shoulders.

"Kentucky, we're asshole buddies, aren't we?" he asked.

Kentucky was moved. Nobody had ever admitted to being his asshole buddy before, not even Partin. It was difficult for him to cope with such affection. Tears filled his eyes so he could not see. Chamberlin gently took the .45 from his hand.

"Don't worry about Captain Brown," he said. "He'll be taken care of."

The engineers had left a bulldozer in L Company's area. They had some work left to do on the company street.

Soon after the episode with Kentucky, Sergeant Browne got drunk. He decided to finish the task Kentucky had failed to do. Only he was smarter than Kentucky. He would make it look like an accident. Instead of a bullet he was going to use the bulldozer like a tank and run over him. Even though he was so drunk he could barely stand, he managed to mount the big machine and get it started. He had never driven a bulldozer before but had handled the controls of a tank once in training. Soon he had the dozer lurching around as he experimented with the controls. But he had to turn it around before he could head for where he thought Captain Brown was. That took time and gave Neathery and Chamberlin a chance to act.

Chamberlin approached the dozer from the operator's side and started talking to Browne. Neathery, even though he was also drunk, had enough sense to realize his buddy was making a mistake. He approached the dozer from the other side.

"Bob, you're not supposed to be driving that dozer," warned Chamberlin.

"I'm going to squash Captain Brown," bellowed Browne. "He's a disgrace to our name and the United States Army. They'll give me a medal for it. I'll be a hero."

"No they won't," said Chamberlin. "They'll put you in the stockade just like they would have Kentucky. Besides, I'll be in trouble too for letting you do it. Don't you care anything about me?"

"No they won't," said Browne, "You're a hero too. They're scared of heroes."

As he was operating the levers to turn the dozer, the track on Neathery's side stopped. Neathery seized the moment to jump up on the track and onto the dozer. He snatched the key from the ignition and Browne was immobilized.

"You son-of-a-bitch, Jack, come back here with my key," hollered Browne at a retreating Neathery.

Browne jumped off the dozer to chase Neathery. The ground seemed to turn from horizontal to vertical as he fell on his face.

Chamberlin helped him up and maneuvered him back to his tent and bunk.

Later that same day Chamberlin was approached by Sergeant Davidson.

"What's this I hear about Captain Brown volunteering the company to go back up on the line so he can earn enough combat time to get his CIB?" asked Davidson.

"Well, yes, I know he needs more combat time to earn a CIB," answered Chamberlin. "He was only on line about two weeks and you need thirty days to be eligible for a CIB. But I haven't heard anything about him volunteering us for combat again."

"Well, Lieutenant, you'd better find out," said Davidson, "because if it's true, his life ain't worth shit."

"I'll talk to him," offered Chamberlin.

Later he spoke to Captain Brown. "Captain Brown, there's a rumor going around that you have volunteered the company for combat duty. Is that true?"

Captain Brown was taken aback. He decided not to admit that he had offered to move the company into a blocking position behind the MLR, which would have given him credit toward his CIB. He could not wait to be awarded his CIB. He had fantasized a big awards ceremony with General Ruffner pinning the badge on his chest. But he sensed something sinister in Chamberlin's low, barely audible voice meant for his ears alone.

"No, that's not true," he lied.

"Good," said Chamberlin. "because your life wouldn't be worth shit if it was."

That night Chamberlin went to bed early. The last few days had been hectic. He was tired. He shared a tent with Captain Brown.

Captain Brown was scared. It was not like being frightened of incoming mortar rounds. Now he feared the unknown. What had Chamberlin meant? Had it been a threat from Chamberlin, himself, or a more general danger from the men of the company? He needed a drink and someone to talk to. He went over to see his friend, Captain Gatsis, in K Company. They had come from the States together and joined the unit at the same time.

They had a few drinks and talked. "Andy, what would you do if somebody in your company threatened to kill you?" asked Brown.

"Why?" asked Gatsis. "Has that happened to you?"

"Well, no," said Brown. "But what if it did? How would you handle it?"

"Oh, I don't know, Les," replied Gatsis. "You can't expect all your men to like you. There's always bound to be some malcontents. The important thing is that they respect you."

A few more drinks and Brown's resolve was fortified. By God, his men were going to respect him! Starting tomorrow they were going to shape up.

He staggered back to his company and entered his sleeping quarters. As he switched on the light—the company now had power furnished by generators—Chamberlin partially woke. At first he thought he was on the MLR and that Brown was an enemy entering his bunker. He reached out and grabbed Brown by the leg just above the knee. Almost immediately he knew it was Brown, but he pretended he did not. He squeezed with all his strength and reached for a dagger with his other hand.

Captain Brown was terrified. Chamberlin's hand felt like a steel clamp.

"Al, Al, wake up. It's me, Captain Brown," he whimpered.

Chamberlin savored the moment for several seconds while Brown tried unsuccessfully to pull away. Finally he relaxed his grip and replaced the dagger in its scabbard.

"Sorry," he said. "I was having a nightmare."

He turned his back on Brown and went back to sleep with a faint smile on his lips.

Brown lay wide awake in complete terror.

15

The next day Captain Brown did clamp down on the men. At a formation he laid down some rules. There was to be reveille at 0630 hours every morning, followed by police call before breakfast. This was something that Chamberlin had not experienced since joining the unit. Boots were to be shined. Living areas would be inspected every day. Days would be spent either on work details or training classes. Military courtesy was to be enforced at all times. The uniform of the day would be posted and was to be adhered to. There would be no more drinking until after 1800 hours.

The men were mad. It rumbled through the ranks like an approaching thunderstorm. This is the thanks we get for fighting our asses off, the combat veterans thought. They had been promised rest and relaxation. Instead they got work and chickenshit.

Again it was up to Chamberlin to calm the men down after Captain Brown had stirred them up. He did the best he could. He spoke gently to them but reminded them of the stark reality of the situation. Captain Brown was their company commander.

Two young second lieutenants, Roberts and Rogers, joined the company. Sergeant Sides rotated back to the States. Bob Browne became the company's first sergeant. Captain Brown moved out of the sleeping quarters he had been sharing with Chamberlin. He did not want to spend another night near such a crazy killer. Roberts and Rogers moved in with Chamberlin.

There was a lot of tension in the air. Chamberlin spent most of his time fraternizing with his buddies, Bob Browne and Jack Neathery, along with other members of the second platoon. In fact, he had the new officers assigned to the first and third platoons and retained the leadership of the second platoon, along with his executive officer's duties.

Things did not go well with the daily inspections. It was impossible for the men to shine split leather combat boots even if they had shoe polish. Most of the men did not have shoe polish and if they did they threw it away so they would have an excuse. But Captain Brown never made the inspections and Chamberlin used them just to visit with men, not to criticize them. Roberts and Rogers sort of followed Chamberlin's lead. Captain Brown never really knew what was going on with the men.

Chamberlin did not attempt to shine his boots, nor did he conform to the uniform of the day edict. That would have meant removing his daggers, grenade pouch, and .45 from his cartridge belt, along with the thongs tying them down. This was his way of rebelling against chickenshit and Captain Brown.

Battalion decided to have a full field inspection of all the troops to make sure each soldier had all his equipment and that it was in good repair. This was something the battalion had not been able to do while on the line. So the officers were rusty. Manuals had to be researched and memorized about how the men should lay out their stuff. Everything had to be uniform.

Captain Brown held a meeting with his officers. He oriented them about the big inspection. He told them he wanted them to hold practice inspections with their platoons until the men got everything perfect. He wanted L Company to look the best. He said he had noticed a lot of fraternization between certain officers and enlisted men, a reference to the brotherhood Chamberlin had with his men. He wanted none of that in his company. He wanted military courtesy observed at all times. This was the key to discipline, and discipline was the key to victory in combat.

Chamberlin mused as Brown talked. What a bunch of shit. Schoolboy stuff. It has nothing to do with combat efficiency. Just more harassment of the men. He leaned back on the bunk he was sitting on, closed his eyes, and tried to block out the military foolishness. The new officers listened intently to Brown's instructions.

Finally Brown asked, "Are there any questions?"

There were none.

Brown repeated the question to make a point. "Lieutenant Chamberlin, are there any questions?"

Chamberlin thought for a moment. It really was not a situation where you could call chickenshit chickenshit, unless you wanted to hang yourself. But he refused to acquiesce to this little bastard.

"Captain Brown, you leave me speechless," he said.

The new officers wondered what in hell was going on. The cold hostility from Chamberlin toward Brown and the fear of Chamberlin by Brown was as obvious as it was ambiguous to the unknowing. They dared not get involved.

Lieutenants Roberts and Rogers did their research in the manual about field inspections. Chamberlin went to the second platoon and informed them of the coming inspection and then shot the shit with them in a fraternal manner.

Captain Brown retreated to his quarters and poured

himself a stiff drink of scotch. What the hell was he going to do about Chamberlin? On the one hand he wished he could be like him, have his guts, have his control of his men. On the other hand he knew he could not be like him. So he worshipped and hated him at the same time, for being what he could not be. He could not fraternize with the enlisted men because they did not like him. So the army's nonfraternization policy fit his personality. He got no natural respect from the men, so the policy of military courtesy made up for his inability to earn respect. He envied the respect all the men had for Chamberlin. He worried that his new officers would be influenced by him. He poured himself another drink, even though it was early in the day—long before 1800 hours.

The next day Captain Brown called Chamberlin over to him. He was with a small group, the company clerk, Sergeant Browne and Lieutenants Roberts and Rogers. He had a big smile on his face.

"Look what I've got for you, Al," he said as he handed Chamberlin a small blue case.

Chamberlin opened it. Inside were a Silver Star medal and ribbon.

"Here's the commendation to go with it," continued the captain.

Chamberlin's eyes lit up as he read the words about his action on Eerie. He did not know exactly what to say. Finally he looked at Sergeant Browne and said, "Thanks. Did any other awards come through?"

Captain Brown assumed he was talking to him. "No, yours was the only one so far," he said. "We're still working on the others. Maybe I'll get my CIB soon."

Corporal Schiefer and Sergeant Browne lowered

144

their eyes to hide their feelings. Lieutenants Roberts and Rogers still did not know what in hell was happening. Captain Brown thought that Chamberlin would now shape up and be cooperative because he had given him his Silver Star.

The day of the big inspection came. The men laid their shelter halves on the ground and displayed their equipment on them. As the men stood at ease before their things, Major Moore and an entourage of lesser officers walked slowly along inspecting the men and their gear. Chamberlin brought up the rear. They came to Kentucky. He had on a pair of non-government-issue combat boots for the occasion. They were the kind made out of glossy leather that you could shine and they laced all the way instead of having buckles for the top part. They were well-shined and looked nice. In fact they looked especially nice. Kentucky had a decorative way of lacing them, not the normal Army way. Chamberlin was proud of Kentucky.

Major Moore did not say anything about Kentucky's boots. But Captain Isham, I Company's commanding officer, said, "Soldier, is that the way you lace your boots?"

"Yes, Sir," answered Kentucky.

Chamberlin was even more proud of him.

"But that's not the Army way to lace boots," continued a provoked Isham. "Who told you you could lace them like that?"

"Nobody, Sir, I figured it out myself," said Kentucky.

Captain Isham turned to Chamberlin. "See to it that he corrects those shoelaces, Lieutenant," he said.

"No big deal," answered Chamberlin. "He only wears them for inspections and Sunday Mass."

Captain Isham was unaccustomed to such insolence, but he knew the reputation of Chamberlin. He

145

knew that he had led the charge to rescue his company on T-Bone. He also noticed that he was still wearing the twin daggers, one of which it was rumored he had pulled on Captain Brown in a fit of rage. He decided to move on.

But soon he found another discrepancy. He pointed to a display of knife, fork, and spoon on Neathery's shelter-half.

"Is that the proper order to lay out eating utensils?" he asked Chamberlin almost in a friendly, inquisitive manner.

"Beats the hell out of me," replied Chamberlin.

This was just too much for Captain Isham to take. "You'd better check your manual, Lieutenant," he snapped.

He turned quickly and moved on to catch up with the other members of the inspecting party. He did not want to be stuck too far back with Chamberlin.

Chamberlin smiled derisively behind his back. He remembered well the reports that Captain Isham had called in artillery on his own troops when they had been overrun on T-Bone. He had had strong overhead cover for himself, but most of his men were in open trenches and exposed to the artillery as much as the enemy. Though this tactic was lauded by some as brilliant and courageous, Chamberlin could not imagine a situation where he would ever call in artillery on his own men just to hold a piece of terrain, or protect his own ass. To him that was the coward's way. He thought that engaging the enemy in hand-to-hand combat was wiser and safer— certainly more courageous.

After the inspection, Major Moore and Captains Brown and Isham went to Brown's CP to discuss the inspection. Chamberlin stayed outside and mingled with the men as they put away their things. They bitched and laughed at the situation and the inspecting officers. Neither Chamberlin nor the men considered Chamberlin a party to the military harassment. He was one of them.

Inside Brown's CP, Captain Isham spoke up about Chamberlin's insubordinate behavior.

"Les, you've got to do something about Chamberlin," he said. "If you don't he'll undermine all you're trying to do and sabotage the combat effectiveness of your men. You can't win in battle unless you have the complete loyalty and control of your men. I know. I've been there."

"But Chamberlin was a good combat officer," said Major Moore. "Pierce and Moroney never had any complaints about him. I don't know what's come over him."

"What do you think I should do?" asked Captain Brown meekly.

"Well Les, why don't you think about it and I'll set up an appointment with Colonel Spottswood for you," said Major Moore. "He should be informed of this."

Captain Brown spent the rest of the day thinking about it. As carefully as a prosecuting officer in a court-martial, he listed the charges against Chamberlin. He had trouble with his list. He could not very well complain about Chamberlin threatening his life. That would make him appear weak. He could not mention the girls in camp. There was no evidence. None of the men would testify against Chamberlin. They would incriminate themselves. Finally he settled on fraternizing with the enlisted men, drinking beer with the men before 1800 hours, not adhering to the uniform of the day, and, above all, inciting the men to mutiny against him. He was pleased with his work. He took it to the clerk for typing.

Soon after breakfast the next day, Colonel Spottswood called Captain Brown and told him he would see him and Chamberlin at 0900 hours in his CP.

"Yes, Sir," said Captain Brown. "Is it all right if I bring two enlisted men with me. They need to learn a lesson too."

"Who are they?" asked Spottswood.

"Sergeant Browne and Sergeant Neathery," said Brown.

Spottswood had heard of both of them and knew they had been put in for medals for heroic action on Eerie and Baldy along with Chamberlin. He wondered what Brown's hidden agenda was.

"Sure," he said. "Why not?"

So Captain Brown led his three men up the slight slope to the Colonel's CP.

The Colonel offered them drinks. Captain Brown accepted a shot of scotch. Sergeants Browne and Neathery looked at Chamberlin for their lead.

"No, thanks," said Chamberlin. "I don't drink on duty."

"So, what brings you here?" asked Spottswood.

Captain Brown looked at his list of charges and was going to read them to the colonel. A side glance at Chamberlin noted the cold steel daggers at his hips. A vision of Chamberlin pulling a dagger on him flashed across his mental screen. He handed the paper to Spottswood.

Colonel Spottswood read the charges carefully. He was not completely surprised. He knew that Chamberlin was a strong individual and rumors had reached him about Brown's cowardice in combat.

"These are serious charges," he said. "What do you have to say for yourself, Lieutenant?"

"I don't know," said Chamberlin. "What are the charges?"

"Haven't you explained the charges to him, Captain?" asked Spottswood.

"Well, no, Sir. I haven't had a chance to," said Brown.

"Lieutenant, Captain Brown says that you are not co-operating with him in running the company, that you are disobeying some of his orders." Colonel Spottswood had deliberately diluted the charges. "Why can't you work things out between you and get along with each other?"

After a moment of silence Chamberlin blurted out, "Because I have no respect for him."

Captain Brown looked at Chamberlin meekly. "But why, Al?" he whined.

"You know damn well why," continued Chamberlin. "I can't stand your guts. Or I should say lack of guts."

Chamberlin hesitated briefly. Nobody said anything. Sergeant Browne looked at Neathery. They both lowered their eyes and waited for the hammer to drop on Chamberlin. Captain Brown looked beseechingly at Spottswood. The Colonel looked at Chamberlin and wondered what in hell was he going to say to extricate himself.

Chamberlin went on. "You've treated the men like shit every since you took over the company. Before we went on line all you did was brag about what you were going to do in combat. Then when we did go on line you were scared shitless. I can understand a person not having much courage in combat, but when that person treats others like dirt and expects them to obey and respect him—well, I just can't stand that."

Chamberlin stopped again.

Finally Spottswood asked, "But what's this about you drinking beer with enlisted men?"

"Yes, Sir, I have drunk beer with some of my men once in a while," admitted Chamberlin. "But I don't see

149

anything wrong with that. We fought together. We saved each others' lives. They're my circle of friends. Why shouldn't we share a beer? We shared more than that on Eerie and Baldy. But I don't drink much."

"What about the charge that you are turning the men against Captain Brown?" inquired Spottswood.

"I've never tried to turn the men against him," denied Chamberlin. "I never had to. In fact, several times I've had to remind them that he is their company commander, whether they like it or not. Also, on at least three occasions I've stopped men from trying to kill him."

"That is very serious," said the Colonel. "Who are those men?"

There was another long pause. Silence stood still.

Captain Brown was ambivalent. To learn that men wanted to kill him was terrifying. To hear Chamberlin hang himself pleased him.

Sergeant Browne was worried. Would Chamberlin let him down? Would they both be court-martialed?

Sergeant Neathery worried about his buddy, Bob. He figured Chamberlin could take care of himself.

Colonel Spottswood waited.

Chamberlin spoke again. "Their names are immaterial," he said. "But they are men of great courage."

Colonel Spottswood looked at the charges again. He mused for a moment. What should the army do, reward or punish courage? He saw this as a mere matter of incompatibility between courage and cowardice. Slowly he tore up the charges.

"I want you people to go back to your company and work things out among you," he said.

Captain Brown could not wait to leave. What he had planned as a triumphant victory had turned into a disas-

150

trous exposé of his inadequacies. He was now afraid to bring up why he had brought Sergeants Browne and Neathery. He led the exodus from the tent as fast as he could. Chamberlin brought up the rear.

When they were a few feet away from the tent, Spottswood stuck his head out and said in a low voice, "Chamberlin, can I see you for a minute?"

Not knowing what to expect, Chamberlin retraced his steps to the CP.

"I'm going to have another drink," said Spottswood. "How about you?"

"Maybe I will have a beer, Sir," agreed Chamberlin.

Spottswood tried to be stern. "I'm a little disappointed in you, Chamberlin," he said. "You were such a good officer in combat that we had great expectations of you."

"I'm sorry, Sir," said Chamberlin as he sipped his beer. "But I can't respect a coward who treats his men like dirt."

Spottswood mused for a moment. He did not want to lose an officer like Chamberlin. "How would you like to be transferred to I Company? They lost a lot of officers and Captain Isham needs an executive officer."

"I don't think so, Sir," said Chamberlin. As long as he was being honest, he thought, he might as well go all the way. Besides, he realized now that Spottswood was on his side. "I didn't think too much of his calling in artillery on his own men on T-Bone. I don't think we would get along either."

"How about K Company?" offered Spottswood. "They're short of officers, too."

"Well, Captain Gatsis is a very close friend of Captain Brown," said Chamberlin. "So I don't think that would work out either. I wouldn't mind going to M Company though. I have a lot of respect for Lieutenant Malone."

"Unfortunately, Malone has a full contingent of officers right now," said Spottswood. "But there's a couple of other possibilities. A new general has just been assigned to Division and needs an aide. He's looking for an officer with a good combat record like you. You would have a good chance if you wanted the position. There is also an opening for an instructor back at the School of Standards."

Chamberlin thought about being a general's aide. He knew that his chances of another promotion would be enhanced, but could he fit into the spit-and-polish chickenshit? Could he kiss some general's ass if he didn't like him? He probably could, but would he want to? He thought not. Besides, he had now decided that he probably would not make the Army his career. So bucking for another promotion was not his cup of tea. He would put in his time in Korea, finish his three years in the Army and then go back to civilian life where he wouldn't have to take orders from some military prick. If he didn't like his boss, he could always quit. Plus, he was not sure he was smart enough to be a general's aide.

"Sir, I don't think I'm cut out to be a general's aide," he said, "but I wouldn't mind being an instructor."

"Okay, Chamberlin, I'll see what I can do and will let you know," said Spottswood.

"Thank you, Sir," said Chamberlin. "Is that all, Sir?"

"Yes, that's all," said Spottswood. "Good luck, son."

They exchanged salutes.

The next day orders came through. Chamberlin was to report to the School of Standards in Wonju.

16

The School of Standards was a short stopover for new replacements of the 45th Division. During operation "Counter," the 45th had suffered many casualties. The wounded and the dead had to be replaced. The fodder of war had to be replenished. To help the new men adapt to the reality of their new life with the prospects of death, they were funneled through this educational pipeline before being dispersed to the various units of the division. It was a brief review of all they had learned in Basic Training about how to kill.

Chamberlin arrived at the school in his full combat gear, twin daggers, grenades, .45 Colt, and leather thongs. He was like a citizen from a foreign country dressed in his native costume. He was a citizen of combat and still felt comfortable in the riggings of a warrior.

Not that the other cadre at the school were not combat veterans. Most of them were. It was just that they had remained relatively uniform in character as well as dress. Whereas Chamberlin had stood out in character, action, and choice of tools of battle. It was a persona that had served him well when needed and he did not wish to relinquish it and fade back into uniformity, the hallmark of mediocrity.

Captain Templeton, the school's commanding officer, asked Chamberlin to report to him soon after his arrival.

"Lieutenant, what is your T.O. & E. weapon?" he asked matter-of-factly.

"It's an M2 carbine, Sir," said Chamberlin. "But on the line, company commanders and executive officers carried .45s."

"Need I remind you that you're not on the line here and that you are not a company commander or an executive officer?" said Templeton. "You are an instructor, and I will expect you to carry your T.O. & E. weapon and adhere to the uniform of the day."

Chamberlin could think of no argument. "Yes, Sir," he said. "Is that all, Sir?"

Back in his quarters Chamberlin removed the armament and thongs from his cartridge belt and stowed them in his duffle bag. He went to supply and drew out a carbine. He did not turn in the .45. To him it was a gift from Moroney.

Chamberlin fit in well at the school. He lived in a large tent with several other combat officers, all lieutenants. Captains had their own tent. He got along well with his peer officers. He taught classes in bayonet and unarmed combat mostly. He had learned these skills well at Fort Dix, New Jersey, in 1951 when he had first entered the service as a new second lieutenant. His recent battle experiences lent authenticity to his classes. During his free time he kept in shape by playing volleyball and exercising.

Wonju was a fairly large city with lots of shops and other attractions for the U.S. servicemen. As he was walking along one of the narrow streets one evening Chamberlin saw a very beautiful Korean girl in one of the small shops. She was selling wares. There were many beautiful girls in Korea, but this one caught his eye because she had gorgeously large breasts. Immediately his appetite was whetted.

154

He went into the shop to reconnoiter the situation. The girl could speak enough English so they could converse. He asked if he could come by later to see her when she was off duty. She agreed.

In her boudoir there was no pretense. She knew what Chamberlin's mission was and was perfectly willing to abet him in accomplishing it. Her price was a little steeper than average but he was willing to pay a little extra for such a luscious handful.

But when they got down to action she insisted that he wear protection. This did not agree with his idea of good intercourse, but he went along with it. He wanted to warm her up by caressing her tits for a while, but she seemed unresponsive to his efforts. Sort of an unnecessary waste of time. So he plunged on into the meat of his mission. She was dry and not as adept as her appearance might have led one to believe. So, all in all, it was not a completely satisfying experience.

One of the duties that all the lieutenants at the school had to pull was Officer of the Day. Among other duties, the OD had to make the rounds of several places near the school that the young American men would frequent to relieve their pent-up passions. It was against Army regulations for military personnel to be in these places of ill repute.

Chamberlin pulled OD duty soon after he came to the school. With a driver and his authoritative OD band around his left bicep, he set out in a jeep on his mission of morality, to keep GIs out of the local dens of iniquity. The first stop was down by the large river that ran pass Wonju and the school. A large community of camp followers lived there.

When he dismounted from the jeep to walk among the crude huts looking for his wayward fellow soldiers,

Chamberlin was surrounded by a throng of Korean kids asking for candy, soap, cigarettes, money, or whatever they thought he might have to offer. The OD band on his shirt sleeve meant nothing to them. His silver lieutenant's bar did. It meant he was an officer—financially better off than an enlisted man.

Almost before he realized it, a young Korean girl wearing glasses moved close to his front. Her head was just above his belt buckle, as her eyes looked up and met his. She was not especially attractive, even as kids go—certainly not the normal sex object. But with deft fingers she opened his fly and quickly had her hand on his penis, which rose to the occasion instantly.

"Sucka hachi?" she asked. "Me number one sucka hachi girl."

The facts that her mouth was just about the right height, that she was so enthusiastic and confident, that she asked for no renumeration, that they were in a public place where such behavior was normally taboo in Chamberlin's book, all added excitement to the idea. But he quickly, though gently, removed her tantalizing fingers and closed his fly.

"No, no," he said softly. "Not here. Not now." His gentle touch and look indicated, however, maybe later.

Chamberlin continued on with his tour of the hotspots around the camp. He finished out his twenty-four hours of OD duty.

All the while the memory of the touch of the little Korean girl's fingers on his genitals simmered in his mind.

As soon as he was off duty he returned to the riverside shantytown to look for the girl. He was not really worried about getting caught. He was an officer and could bluff his way. And there was a certain thrill to sneaking around where you were not supposed to be—breaking the rules. He remembered well all the off-limits geisha houses he had visited in Japan after World War II when he was an enlisted man with the Occupation Forces. Ever since he had been a kid, he hadn't liked being told he could not do something.

He did not have to look long. She was waiting for him. She led him quickly to the small hut she shared with her family. She removed his boots at the door. Her parents grinned as she led him past them into a small bedroom where the family slept on mats on the straw floor. Swiftly and smoothly she plied her trade. She did all the work. She directed him to the mat they were to use. She unbuckled his belt and opened his fly and removed his pants. She folded them neatly and put them on the floor nearby. Then she did her sucka hachi routine.

Chamberlin had experienced oral sex before, but never anything like this. Her fingers, lips and tongue tantalized and caressed his genitals gently and tenderly, as though they were to be adored and cherished—like a child taking pleasure in an ice-cream cone. She brought him to a wild climax. In the rush of emotions he held her head tenderly and stroked her dark hair affectionately. Then she washed him. He gave her two dollars. Her parents grinned again as he departed. During his stay at the School of Standards he was to return many times to visit his little sucka hachi girl. He brought her candy, soap, and other goodies, and always paid her the going rate of two dollars.

About two weeks after he came to the school and about one week after he had had sex with the girl with the big bust, Chamberlin was down by the river one day. He had to urinate. While pissing on the sandy shore he

157

felt a burning sensation in his urethral canal. When he finished, he milked it down as he had been taught to do in short-arm inspections. There was a tiny bit of pus discharge from his penis. *Son-of-a-bitch,* he thought. *I've got the clap.*

He returned to the camp immediately and checked in with an Army doctor, a young first lieutenant, who gave him a shot of penicillin in the rump. It cured the clap. There was no more urinary stress. Unlike most things in the Army, this sort of treatment was confidential and not recorded even on your medical record. So he was safe there.

He had been told that the incubation period for gonorrhea was two weeks, so he could not figure out the origin of his infection. *Was it the girl he had had sex with over three weeks ago before he came to the school, or the one about a week before the advent of the infection, the one with the big tits?* This puzzled him.

Meanwhile back at his parent unit, Sergeant Browne was rotated back to the States as were many of the other members of L Company. Captain Brown had been relieved when Chamberlin was sent to the School of Standards. He was also glad when Sergeant Browne left the unit. Now the only member left of that terrible trio was Neathery. And Neathery was not basically a troublemaker. Captain Brown felt he could deal with him.

Now he could also deal with another subject that he had been sitting on for some time, not knowing exactly how to handle it. It was the matter of all the recommendations for medals Chamberlin had made for his men after their heroism on Eerie and Baldy.

Chamberlin's had already been processed. There was nothing he could do about those even if he wanted to. But there were a slew of others that Corporal Schiefer had never had time to type up because of other clerical duties. Captain Brown had kept him busy with other administrative paper work.

Corporal Schiefer also rotated about the same time that Browne did. Now Captain Brown had a new clerk to break in. He did not think that it was fair that this new clerk should be saddled with a lot of leftover paperwork, time-consuming work that he was unfamiliar with. So he took it upon himself to help his new clerk. He sorted through the box of statements and recommendations in the privacy of his CP. He decided to let only one be processed on through channels, a Silver Star for Neathery for his action on Eerie. Since Neathery was still with his company, it seemed the only fair and proper thing to do. It would be good for the morale of his men. The rest he rated as nonessential paperwork and used his prerogative as company commander to reject them. In case there were any questions, he tore them all into tiny bits to cover his tracks. He burned them slowly so as to not make much smoke as he sipped Scotch and water.

Later in the fall, the 179th Infantry Regiment had an elaborate awards ceremony. The heroes of the battles on Baldy, Eerie, T-Bone and Porkchop were gathered together and presented their medals for valor and gallantry. Captains Brown and Gatsis, along with others, also were awarded their much coveted CIBs. But many were missing from the gala. Many had rotated, many were wounded, and many were dead. Much heroism had gone unnoted, perhaps even unseen. Some instances were forgotten or lost in the shuffle of military red tape—others arbitrarily rejected by some contemptible little officer like Captain Brown. Chamberlin was not invited.

Back at the School of Standards, Chamberlin was ignorant of the awards ceremony. He continued on with his duties as an instructor. He also continued to break the rules and get into trouble.

The officers at the school had a club where they drank and socialized. Chamberlin make it a point not to drink much, and socializing with other officers was not his favorite thing to do. So he was rarely seen in the Officers Club.

However, on one occasion he did attend a birthday dinner party for Captain Templeton. It was sort of a command performance at which all the officers were expected to be. Several of the officers escorted Korean girls. One Korean girl stood out. She was extraordinarily beautiful. She had a gorgeous body, even more gorgeous than the girl from whom he might have got the clap. Her face was pretty as a doll. She had rosy cheeks and perfectly proportioned features. But aside from noting her beauty and envying the officer she was with, Chamberlin did not think about her any more for a few days.

In the meantime he had befriended a Corporal Tom Ryan, one of the enlisted cadre at the school. They taught some classes together, went on patrol of off-limits places together, and had some things in common to talk about. Ryan was from the 120th Engineers and had helped build bunkers and gun positions on Baldy. He also enjoyed the pleasures of the flesh as did Chamberlin, and occasionally they visited a small community of peasants to the west of the camp to help some of the local ladies support their families.

On one tour of duty as OD, Chamberlin patrolled clear to the outskirts of the aforementioned community. Officially, he was looking for wayward GIs. Whenever he found any he would send them back to camp without pressing charges against them. He treated them as he would want to be treated in the same circumstances. Unofficially, he was reconnoitering for potential places for his own personal pleasure. As he peeked into a small dimly lit hut he saw the beautiful girl who had graced the recent party on the arm of a captain. There was another young girl with her.

Chamberlin took note of the location of the hut. The following evening he and Tom Ryan returned. They decided beforehand that they would pretend the girls were not for hire. Actually they did not know they were, so it was not exactly a pretense. They would treat them like ladies, try to make love to them, and seduce them as though they were American girls. Ryan was willing to try to make out with the other girl, while Chamberlin made his play for the luscious one.

Things did not work as planned. The beautiful girl was a pro. She demanded money up front.

"No, no," lied Chamberlin. "We just want to be friends and talk to you."

This did not please the girls. They were accustomed to getting paid for their time. They remained aloof to the men's unconventional advances, and nothing of great social significance happened for the short while that Chamberlin and Ryan were there.

And it was a short time. Almost as if summoned as a rescue, a jeep pulled up outside. It was the guard patrol led by Sergeant Hooker from the school. The sergeant took their names and told them they were in an off-limits area and should return to camp, which they did.

Chamberlin was disappointed, but thought nothing more about it until several days later. Then he received a communication from Captain W.C. Kusener, by command of General Ruffner, that stated that he had solicited an enlisted man to accompany him to an off-limits Korean house. *That son-of-a-bitch Hooker turned us in,* realized Chamberlin. General Ruffner proposed to impose punishment pursuant to Article 15, unless he demanded a trial by court-martial. He was ordered to reply by indorsement stating whether he demanded a trial. He was also permitted to submit any matter in mitigation, extenuation, or defense.

So Chamberlin replied by indorsement. He acknowledged that he was in an off-limits house, but said he was there to invite a Korean girl to a party at the officers club. He explained that the girl was a frequent guest at the officers club. He said he had taken an enlisted man with him for protection. He did not ask for a court-martial.

The next indorsement to this correspondence was the punishment under Article 15 meted out by General Ruffner. Chamberlin was ordered to forfeit $135 (the highest price he had ever paid for a piece of ass he never got). He was also reprimanded for deliberately transgressing the standing orders of the Army Commander and setting a deplorable example for his subordinates. His conduct was considered to have been extremely prejudicial to good order and military discipline. His solicitation of an enlisted man to accompany him upon this illegal venture constituted an intolerable aggravation of his offense. It was expected that his future conduct would set an example of decorum worthy of emulation by his associates in the service.

Chamberlin wondered why some officers got away with doing the same thing other officers did not. He also wondered if General Ruffner had had any Korean pussy yet. But he would have to admit he had gotten away with a lot already. He had been pretty lucky.

Soon after this incident, he was ordered back to his unit. In his absence he had been transferred to M Company. The 179th was going back on line soon, and all their men were needed, especially proven veterans like Chamberlin. By now replacements had filled the holes left by the rotated, the wounded, and the dead.

In early November Chamberlin reported to Captain White, the new CO of M Company.

17

After Chamberlin arrived at M Company he lost no time in replacing the armament to his cartridge belt—his daggers, .45, and the thongs to tie them down. To him they were the practical weapons of battle and it was practical to tie them down so he could draw one quickly, like the gunfighters and cowboys of the old West. To others, such as Captain White, they were like a chip on his shoulder daring anyone to call him on them, a challenge to legitimate authority, a slap in the face of the average soldier who obeyed the rules.

Captain White had reviewed Chamberlin's file and had talked to Captain Brown about him. He thought he was well prepared to deal with him. He decided to nip things in the bud and let him know who was boss. He called Chamberlin in for a routine talk about his assignment in the company.

"Lieutenant, welcome to our company," he said with a pleasant smile. "I understand you're a good man with a machine-gun. That's good. I want you to take over the machine-gun platoon. While we're still back in reserve you'll have a chance to get acquainted with your men and teach them the finer points of the use of machine-gun fire in combat. I think you will find that M Company has a fine group of officers. Lieutenant Black has the Recoilless Weapons Platoon and Lieutenant Brownly has the Mortar Platoon. They are both fine young gentlemen."

"Yes, Sir, I know Lieutenant Brownly," said Chamberlin. "We went through Benning together."

"They're out in the field today, but you'll meet them for dinner tonight. We all eat together," continued White. "By the way, Lieutenant, the only officers who are allowed to wear .45s are company commanders. Also leather thongs are prohibited. General Ruffner doesn't like them."

"Well this one was given to me by Lieutenant Moroney when he rotated. It has a lot of sentimental value to me," said Chamberlin.

"But it wasn't really his to give to you, was it?" said White.

Chamberlin realized the shallowness of his argument. "No, I guess you're right," he said. "What do you want me to do with it? It's not on anybody's books."

"You should turn it in to supply," said White.

Chamberlin did as he was told.

That evening Captain White introduced his new officer to Lieutenants Black and Brownly. Black's name fit his complexion and his race. He appeared to be an unobtrusive, quiet person who agreed with whatever White said. Brownly was very much the proper gentleman who followed White's lead in behavior and conversation—A typical brown-nose.

Chamberlin was also introduced to a new brand of harassment of the enlisted men. Chow was prepared in a large mess tent. The men lined up outside the tent and filed through the tent to get their food. The cooks and KP personnel dished out the food from the serving line. The men passed on through the tent and out into the open to eat. They sat on the ground, logs, stones, or whatever. They were not allowed to sit on their helmets.

In all of his training Chamberlin had been taught

that, whenever officers and enlisted men shared the same mess facilities, the men ate first. But not here. In the corner of the mess tent was a table for four with chairs set up for the officers. It was in a spot where the men had to pass within inches of the officers just before they got to the serving line. Anything the men did or said was within sight and hearing of the officers. This setup stymied any cussing or horsing around. And, of course, the officers were served before the men were allowed to eat.

Chamberlin got off to a bad start. "Pretty fucking crowded in here, isn't it?" he asked.

White looked at him paternally. "We don't use vulgarity here and we discourage the men from using it too," he moralized. "I have always believed that the use of vulgar language is a sign of a poor vocabulary."

After their food was served Captain White asked them to bow their heads while he said a blessing. Chamberlin ate his meal in silence. Captain White told tea-party jokes. Black and Brownly laughed and responded politely. In the course of the conversation it came out that White had been a professor of English and in the Army Reserves. He had signed up for active duty because the pay was better.

That night in their sleeping quarters, Captain White, Black, and Brownly had some more polite, decent conversations. Chamberlin did some situps and turned in early.

The next morning Chamberlin did not join the officers at their breakfast table. He stood at the end of the line and ate outside like the men. He found a spot a little apart from the men and ate alone.

Captain White was not dumb. He prided himself on his knowledge of human nature. He figured Chamberlin was sulking. He wanted him to feel wanted and be a part of his fine group of officers. When the company lined up to march to the field, he asked Chamberlin to march at the head of the column and set the cadence. Captain White marched the troops as though they were in basic training or on parade. "Hut, two, three, four," he shouted.

Chamberlin had not marched like this for some time, but he did not have any trouble keeping in step with White's cadence counting. However, White did have trouble matching his counting with Chamberlin's stride.

"Keep it at 120 steps per minute," he hollered. "Hut, two, three, four."

Chamberlin thought this was ridiculous, making the men march in step. Close-order drill was for trainees, not combat men. He thought they should be allowed to march at route step. In fact it would have been much more realistic to have them spread out and walk in two single files on each side of the road. That's the way movements were made in combat. Besides, he did not know the difference between 120 and 100 steps per minute. Nor did he give a shit.

He turned to Captain White and said, "Let somebody else lead." He moved out to the side of the column and Lieutenant Black took over the lead spot. Black had rhythm and knew all about White's cadence. He had been marching to it for some time now.

When they were in the field and Chamberlin was alone with his men, he decided to teach them how to fire a free-swinging machine-gun, as he had done on Baldy, by demonstrating it to them. He fired a few bursts into a bank. Almost immediately Captain White was on the radio.

"What's going on over there?" he shouted. He sounded very angry.

"I'm teaching the men how to fire a machine-gun in

a combat situation," replied Chamberlin coolly.

"Well, I'm sure you can teach them without wasting all that ammunition," snapped White.

So the rest of the day Chamberlin taught his men unarmed combat and how to use knives and bayonets in hand-to-hand combat.

Captain White decided that he and Chamberlin were not communicating very well. He would have to do something about it. But it required careful planning, sort of like a well-written lesson plan for one of his English classes, or a session with a failing student. It was important to say the right thing. He scheduled a meeting with Chamberlin the next Sunday after Mass.

The next day the regimental commander, Colonel Jefferson Irvin, gave a pre-combat pep talk to all his officers. Irvin was a young-looking, redheaded bird colonel. He told his officers that they must maintain discipline at all costs in combat. To do this they must not fraternize with the men because familiarity breeds contempt. When they were on the line they should not share the same foxhole or latrine facilities with enlisted men. Military courtesy and non-fraternization build respect, the *sine qua non* for success in battle.

Chamberlin mused about the colonel's words. He must have been doing things all wrong when he shared foxholes and gun positions with his men on Eerie and Baldy. Familiarity might breed contempt, but not necessarily so. Nonfamiliarity could also breed alienation, disrespect, and lack of communications. What officers needed, he thought, was courage. That was the *sine qua non* of battle.

Before White could have his post-Mass meeting with Chamberlin, the regiment moved up to the front lines. Chamberlin's machine-gun platoon was assigned out to two companies, one section to I Company on the right side of the battalion sector, and one section to K Company on the left. None of his guns were attached to L Company. It was as if someone, perhaps the new battalion commander, Major Morgan, was trying to avoid a conflict between Chamberlin and Captain Brown.

Captain White ordered Chamberlin to stay with the section attached to K Company under Captain Gatsis. Chamberlin followed orders, but he also made a trip to his machine-guns with I Company to ascertain exactly where they were, what their targets were and how his men were doing. In the K Company sector he moved into a bunker with some of his men and became as familiar with them as possible.

As soon as they arrived at the MLR, Chamberlin dug out his grenade pouch and the thongs to tie the pouch and his daggers down to his thighs. To hell with General Ruffner's ban.

A few days after their coming on line Chamberlin got a call from Captain White. "I'm going on R and R for four days," said White. "I just found out you have seniority over Black and Brownly."

"Yes, I know," said Chamberlin.

Before, White had always left Black in charge of the company in his absence. Chamberlin did not care, but he had noticed. He had wondered when White would wise up.

"So that means I have to leave the company in your hands while I'm gone," continued White.

"You don't have to if you don't want to," said Chamberlin. "It doesn't matter to me."

"Yes I do," said White. "It's only proper."

"Okay," agreed Chamberlin. "Anything special you want me to do?"

"No, you can carry on pretty much as you have been," said White. "You just have to report over to my CP to sign the morning report each day."

So the next day Chamberlin reported to Captain White's CP, as ordered, to sign the morning report. While there, the company clerk told him there was a problem.

"What is it?" asked Chamberlin.

"Corporal Hardy was driving a jeep for Captain Isham this morning and the captain reported that he had not shaved. So Hardy has to be court-martialed and you have to recommend it," explained the clerk.

Chamberlin knew Hardy and knew that he was a good soldier. He also knew that he was married and had some kids. Court-martialing him would most likely mean a fine and a reduction in grade, a net loss of money to him and his family.

"Have him report to me," ordered Chamberlin.

When he reported Hardy made no excuses. He admitting he had not shaved.

Chamberlin got out the manual on Military Justice. He located the section on company punishment under Article 15, the one so recently used on him. As company commander he could administer company punishment and thereby control the punishment; he could not conduct a court-martial. He gave Hardy company punishment. He was to report to the mess tent each evening after chow and squash cans for thirty minutes each day for one week. There, he thought, now they can't court-martial him. That would be double jeopardy.

Chamberlin called in the company clerk. "Type up the papers for company punishment for Hardy for me to sign," he ordered.

"But, Sir, he was supposed to be court-martialed," said the clerk. "You'll get in trouble."

"Don't worry about me," replied Chamberlin. "Just get the papers ready."

Soon after the papers were finished, signed and sent through proper channels, the phone rang for Chamberlin. It was Major Moore.

"Lieutenant, one of your men was found by Captain Isham this morning unshaven," reported Moore.

"I know," replied Chamberlin. "I've already taken care of it."

"What did you do?" asked Moore.

"I gave him company punishment," answered Chamberlin.

"But you can't do that," said Moore. "He has to be court-martialed."

"I didn't think he deserved to be court-martialed," said Chamberlin.

"But it's Division policy," explained Moore.

"I know, but did anybody ever think about changing that policy?" said Chamberlin.

Major Moore hung up.

A call was quickly put through to Captain White and he returned to his company. His R and R was aborted on the first of four days, before he even got out of Korea. Majors Moore and Morgan agreed that Chamberlin could not be trusted to command a company.

In early December of 1952, K Company was ordered to relieve the company occupying Christmas Tree Ridge. Chamberlin's machine-gun squads attached to K Company made the move also. The move was made at night. It was very dark. The route of march was down a steep slope, made slippery by light snow and frozen ground, then up a narrow road to the christmas tree shaped ridge. No lights were allowed. It was a very difficult move that took most of the night. The men were very tired. When they got into their gun positions, Chamberlin visited both gun squads. He told them to set up their machine-guns, keep two men on each gun and have the rest of the men rest as much as possible. He went to his new CP and rested himself.

As a matter of fact he rested well into the next day, unaware that he was in trouble again. In the afternoon he received a phone call from Captain White.

"Chamberlin, Major Morgan inspected your area this morning and the gun positions and men were filthy," said White. "The positions had not been policed up and the men were dirty and unshaven."

"What time did the Major make his inspection?" asked Chamberlin. "He didn't stop to see me."

"It was around 0800 hours, just after dawn," said White.

"Well, at that time my men did not have any water to clean up with, except what they had in their canteens and the gun jackets," said Chamberlin.

"That's no excuse," said White. "Major Morgan wants you to report to his CP at 1800 hours. I'll send a jeep over for you."

"I don't need a jeep," said Chamberlin. "I can walk."

Chamberlin had never been to the battalion CP before but he knew where it was. It was about a half-mile to the east of his own CP. He had walked the trenches along the line before. This stretch of trenches was occupied by L Company and most of the men knew him or of him. He walked through the long, dark trench unafraid. He knew that the men knew his silhouette and he knew the password if need be. He was not worried about any soldiers with nervous trigger fingers. Most soldiers were reluctant to draw attention to themselves by firing their weapons anyhow.

Chamberlin entered a battalion CP that was warm and well-lit. Major Morgan's desk was near the entrance. Further back in the large field tent were staff officers busy with their battle planning. Captain White and Lieutenant Brownly were also there presumably plotting mortar targets, but perhaps to witness Chamberlin get his comeuppance.

All conversation and activity ceased upon Chamberlin's entrance. All eyes focused on him and Major Morgan.

After their initial saluting, Morgan said, "Take off your jacket and sit down, Chamberlin."

Chamberlin leaned his carbine in a corner and slowly untied his thongs so he could remove his cartridge belt and field jacket. Then he sat.

"Chamberlin, I was in your area this morning and the place was a mess," bellowed Major Morgan.

Finally Chamberlin was going to get it, thought all the eager audience.

"Some of your men hadn't shaved for a week," continued Morgan in a loud scolding voice.

Chamberlin jumped to his feet and towered above the sitting major, who was himself a big man. "That's not true, Sir" he responded in a loud, confident voice.

Major Morgan was taken off guard by such boldness from a junior officer. "Sit down, Chamberlin," he said in a much less threatening tone. "Don't get excited."

Chamberlin sat. There was a pause. Tension in the tent built.

Finally Morgan continued. "What did you inspect your men for after they moved last night?"

"I checked to see that their guns were operating, that they had plenty of ammunition and were ready to fight," said Chamberlin.

Morgan could not argue with that. Chamberlin was beginning to impress him with his audacity. He decided to change the subject.

"We're having a lot of trouble capturing prisoners," he said in a low voice as he leaned forward in his chair toward Chamberlin. "Do you have any ideas on how we could capture some prisoners?"

"I don't know, Sir," said Chamberlin less defensively. "Send out some contact patrols, I guess."

"You want to take out some patrols for me?" asked Morgan eagerly.

"Hell, no," replied Chamberlin.

Chamberlin had already applied for an Inter-FECOM transfer, after he had made his decision not to stay in the Army, following his punishment under Article 15 by General Ruffner. Now he hoped to be able to ride out his remaining months in M Company. Officers of a heavy weapons company did not normally take out patrols.

"You had enough patrol duty before, huh?" said Morgan.

"That's right, Sir" agreed Chamberlin.

"Say, while you're here, you want to show me where your guns are and their primary targets?" asked Morgan. "Here, show me on the war map."

He rose from behind his desk and led Chamberlin to the center of the tent where a large war map was located.

Finally, thought Captain White, *Chamberlin will make a fool of himself.*

Chamberlin picked up the pointer and deftly pointed out exactly what the major had asked. He did so with the expertise of a well-versed instructor teaching a class.

The eyes and ears of the gawking audience followed his every move and word. They suffered many mixed emotions that none of them would have dared admit or express. They were witnessing a type of courage none of them had, did not think one should have, but wished he did have.

When they were finished, Chamberlin put his jacket and cartridge belt on. He bent down with his rear toward the other officers in the tent and carefully tied the thongs in square knots around his thighs. He picked up his carbine with its 120-round clip clinging snugly to its belly, saluted the Major smartly, and walked out of the tent into the darkness. As he retraced his steps back through the maze of trenches to his CP, he was pleased with himself. He smiled, and was friendly and fraternal with all the troops he encountered in the trenches. None of them were officers.

18

Christmas Tree Ridge was more dangerous than the positions K Company had occupied before. At the top of the christmas tree was Bethlehem Point. Beyond Bethlehem Point to the north was a short expanse of no-man's-land extending about 300 yards to Luke's Castle, the foremost Chinese position. At 300 yards, a mediocre marksman could hit a six-inch bull's-eye with fair consistency. One was supposed to be careful about exposing himself to direct view of Luke's Castle, because Chinese snipers were located there.

Chamberlin found that out one day. A jeep came up the road which ended at K Company's CP. Chamberlin's CP was just across the road. The driver stopped to ask directions to some rear echelon unit. He was lost and had inadvertently driven clear up to perhaps the most dangerous part of the MLR of that sector. Chamberlin decided to impress him with the seriousness of his error.

"You want to see where you are?" he asked. "Come on, I'll show you."

The driver got out of his jeep and followed Chamberlin a little further forward to a spot from which they could see Luke's Castle, and from where they could also be seen. Chamberlin pointed to the enemy positions.

"See how close you are to the enemy?" he said. "The Chinese are over there. You're in a very dangerous place."

As if to emphasize his remark a bullet snapped as it passed between their heads. Chamberlin ducked and led the driver back out of sight of the sniper.

"See what I mean?" said Chamberlin.

"Yes, Sir," said the driver. He jumped in his jeep, turned it around and sped down the road.

Chamberlin smiled. *He'll have a war story to tell,* he thought.

Occasionally the Chinese and Americans would exchange a few mortar rounds just to keep each other on their toes. Usually this random shelling did little damage. Soldiers were warned to wear their armored vests and steel helmets when they were outside their bunkers.

One of Chamberlin's gun squads was positioned on a finger ridge running off the main ridge that made up the trunk of the tree, like a bough on a real tree. From there they had a good shot at Luke's Castle. While using his steel helmet to shave in—a common practice—one of Chamberlin's men was hit in the head by shrapnel from one of those random mortar rounds. He had been shaving just outside his bunker in the morning light so he could see better. It was a foggy morning; he figured the Chinese could not see him because he could not see them. He felt safe. He never knew what hit him. He died instantaneously. Perhaps he was one of the lucky ones. Try telling that to his mother.

Chamberlin was beginning to get along well with Captain Gatsis. Every morning he would report to Gatsis's CP to coordinate plans. One night there was a heavy snow fall. While at their morning meeting, which included the artillery forward observer, Lieutenant Stone, there was talk of the snow.

"The snow's so deep it covered my observation port hole," said Stone.

"Why don't you go outside and shovel it out?" asked Chamberlin.

"Not me," said Stone. "I'm not going out there and expose myself to sniper fire."

"What if you need to direct some artillery fire?" continued Chamberlin.

"I don't know," said Stone. "But I'm not going out there."

Ever willing to show his courage and disdain for the faint at heart, Chamberlin said, "I'll do it for you."

He picked up a shovel, went outside and wallowed through the deep snow around the bunker to the observation port hole. He was in direct view of Luke's Castle, from where a sniper had taken a shot at him only days before. His olive-drab parka stood out starkly against the white snow. Quickly he shoveled the snow away from the port hole. Nothing happened. Even the exciting feeling of fear was now gone. *Things are getting boring,* thought Chamberlin. He stood up to his full height when the snow removal job was finished. He looked toward the Chinese lines defiantly, as though to challenge them to make the war more interesting. Was he crazy? Did he need to have bullets flying around him to prove how courageous he was? Did he not have enough medals to take home with him already? In one of her letters, after he had told her about Eerie, his mother had told him, "Stop showing off." She used to tell him that when he was a kid if he showed off trying to get attention. If she were here now, she would tell him again. And he would probably ignore her as he did then.

Speaking of medals, Chamberlin's Distinguished Service Cross had been turned down. It had been approved all the way through Division. General David L. Ruffner had approved it on 20 November, only fourteen days after he had signed the papers punishing Chamberlin for his indiscretion at the School of Standards. Did the irony escape him? Is the worst sometimes the best? The approval was vetoed by Lieutenant General Paul W. Kendall, by Command of General Van Fleet. It was recommended that it be lowered to another Silver Star.

Inside the bunker, Lieutenant Stone was confused. "Should I have gone out there to shovel out the port hole?" he asked Captain Gatsis.

"No," said Gatsis. "You did the normal thing. Chamberlin does things that most men wouldn't do. Nothing seems to bother him much."

"He's crazy," opined First Sergeant O'Leary.

One night K Company was to send out a contact patrol, one of Major Morgan's attempts to capture some prisoners. Chamberlin decided to go up to Bethlehem Point to be close to the action. There was a K Company machine-gun positioned there for support fire if needed.

Soon after the patrol set out toward Luke's Castle it was ambushed by the enemy. Support fire was called for. Artillery and mortar rounds filled the air and saturated the snow-covered terrain with deadly shrapnel. The machine-gun opened fire to lend its meager missiles to the fray.

Chamberlin noted that the gunner was firing the machine gun as he had been trained, in short bursts of three or four rounds from a fixed mount. Soon the gun jammed. Something was wrong. The young gunner could get it to fire only one round at a time. He did not seem to know what to do. Sounds like too much head space, thought Chamberlin.

"Here, let me help you," said Chamberlin.

He quickly unscrewed the barrel, tightened it back up, backed it off two notches for head space adjustment, reloaded, and fired. It worked perfectly. He loosened the clamps and commenced sending streams of support fire out in front of where the patrol was supposed to be. This was exciting, he thought. Not as dangerous as Eerie or Baldy had been, but exciting. He warmed to the task. Soon the stream of tracers started bending in a tell-tale fashion. He had fired the gun so fast that he had burned out the barrel. He had heard that could happen, but this was the first time for him.

"Got another barrel?" he asked.

The gunner produced a spare barrel and soon the gun was back in action. Chamberlin turned it back over to its crew. None of them questioned what he had done, even though they did not know who he was. It added evidence to his theory that combat leadership had nothing to do with rank. It was more a matter of courage, confidence, and perhaps a touch of cockiness. But then, perhaps they had heard of the lieutenant with the leather thongs.

Chamberlin moved back to where the patrol had set out a little while ago. They had suffered casualties and a litter team was supposed to be there to go out to retrieve them. The patrol leader said there was still one man out there wounded. He knew where he was. He needed three men and a stretcher to go with him to bring him back. One of the litter team seemed to be missing. They were short a man. There were several men from K Company standing around but no one volunteered to help go get their fallen comrade.

"I'll go," said Chamberlin.

They went out into no-man's-land and found the wounded soldier. The men proceeded to load him onto the stretcher. Chamberlin had to urinate. He watched for the enemy as he pissed. Then he noticed that one of his thongs was untied. He bent over to secure it.

"Come on, let's go," whispered the patrol leader.

"Don't get your piss hot," Chamberlin whispered back.

They each took a corner of the stretcher and worked their way slowly back along the slippery path to the protection of friendly trenches. Once, one guy slipped and their passenger nearly rolled off the stretcher but they caught him just in time. They handled the casualty very carefully. They had not taken the time to check if he was alive. They did not know he was dead. Nor did the men of K Company know that an officer from M Company had accompanied them on their mission of mercy. He never told them.

During the days following his encounter with Major Morgan, Chamberlin wondered if he had made the right decision when he had said he did not want to take out patrols. He did not want people to think he was a coward. He was afraid. Fear was normal. But he was no coward. He did not want others to think of him as he thought of Captain Brown, who he heard now never left his well-fortified bunker with a personal bodyguard—an ex-boxer—stationed at the entrance. No, he was not that scared. Having people think he was bugged him.

Maybe it would be interesting to go out and capture some prisoners. That would break up the monotony. And it would show Major Morgan, General Ruffner, Captain White, and other military pricks what kind of a combat man he was. He wished he had some men like Bob Browne and Jack Neathery with him again. They would go out with him and bring back a Chink.

Say, that's an idea, he thought. Some of his men from the second platoon were still over there in L Company—Partin, Tally, and Kentucky. He would bet they would go with him. So he paid them a visit and asked if they would volunteer to go in patrol with him.

"Sure," said Kentucky. "We have to go on patrol anyways. I'd rather go with you than these dumb officers in this company."

All three of them agreed. In fact, before he could leave their area Chamberlin had more guys volunteer to go with him than he wanted. Thanks to his buddies, everybody in L Company knew about him. Most of them wanted to be counted in his circle of combat buddies.

Chamberlin returned to his CP. He thought about how he would take out a patrol. First he would have to do some reconnoitering. Maybe he would even go out by himself into no-man's-land and spend a day observing and listening. He would want it all to be very secret—the time, route, everything. He would not even want S2 to know about it. Patrols that were being sent out now by battalion intelligence were often ambushed or running into minefields. He thought it was because they always took the same routes, and at the same time of night. They were predictable. The enemy knew where and when to expect them.

The more he thought of his idea the more excited he got about it. He spent time up at Bethlehem Point with field glasses observing Luke's Castle and the neutral terrain in between. He watched for enemy activity, studied the land for routes of movement and hiding places. He tried to figure out where the Chinese might station listening posts manned by only a few soldiers who could be overcome and captured easily. He thought if he was out there alone closer to their lines he could become even more knowledgeable of their routines. They would become as predictable to him as the American forces seemed to be to them. Maybe they had soldiers hiding close to our lines so they could ascertain our habits. He would not mind running into one if he were out there by himself. He was confident that he could outwit and out-fight any Chink in hand-to-hand combat—even two or three of them—with his full-automatic carbine.

He spent some more time over on the right flank of K Company, studying the slope down toward a small stream where it was thought that the Chinese often had a small listening post. That might be the best area in which to operate. It was a little further away from the main Chinese forces, so one would be less apt to encounter large numbers of the enemy.

He also spent a little more time in L Company's second platoon area talking with Kentucky, Partin, and Tally. They decided on a couple other guys to go with them when Chamberlin had things ready.

It was time to put his plan into action. Chamberlin called Major Morgan.

"Sir, this is Lieutenant Chamberlin," he said. "I've been thinking about your asking me to take out a patrol. I'd like to talk to you about it."

"Good, Lieutenant," replied Major Morgan. "I'm coming over to see Captain Gatsis at 1400 hours today. Meet me in his CP."

"Yes, Sir," said Chamberlin.

Major Morgan listened to Chamberlin explain his plan to take out a patrol of volunteers, his idea of scouting the terrain and preparing beforehand. He was impressed with not only the guts of Chamberlin but also his careful planning. Captain Gatsis, Lieutenant Stone, and Sergeant O'Leary listened in silence. Gatsis and Stone were amazed that Chamberlin had the brass to talk to the battalion commander in such a manner. O'Leary was now sure that Chamberlin was crazy. Battle fatigue manifests itself in many ways. Maybe he was crazy like a fox.

Then Chamberlin dropped his bombshell. "But I don't want anybody to know about my plans. Not even S2."

Major Morgan looked at Chamberlin much like a father might look at a rambunctious son. He was not angry. How could he be angry at such courage? It was his duty to put such courage to good use, not to stymie it. But he could not let anyone thumb his nose at his staff either.

"Lieutenant, I can't let you do that," he said. "My staff would have to know."

"Okay," said Chamberlin. "But those are my conditions."

After the meeting Chamberlin had mixed feelings. He was disappointed in a way. This would have been a chance to be a real hero without having it forced upon him like before on Eerie and Baldy. There was something in him that wanted to be recognized for things like going out to help bring back that dead man when he did not have to. There was also something that prevented him from bragging, or even telling, about it. He did truly miss Bob Browne and Jack Neathery. They could talk, even joke, among themselves about things like that and they would all understand. Maybe it was because each of them was equally courageous, or perhaps equally crazy.

He was also extremely relieved that he would not have to take out any patrols He was also rather smug about how he had handled himself with Major Morgan. He had showed him he was no coward.

But the major was no dummy. The next day Chamberlin was transferred to K Company. Now he would have to take out patrols when his turn came.

19

Captain White was more than willing to get rid of Chamberlin. He did not like rebels. And, though they had been together only a few days before they moved up on the line, he knew all he wanted to know about him. Chamberlin's rebellious behavior against the military code of ethics while at the School of Standards had been brought to White's attention. At first he had tried to give Chamberlin the benefit of the doubt, but Chamberlin had even rebelled against his kind, paternal guidance. Then, when he put him in charge of the company, Chamberlin had fouled up the very first day. It had ruined his cultural trip to Japan. Yes, though he had never visited any of Chamberlin's gun positions on the MLR, White felt competent to judge Chamberlin as incompetent.

But Captain Gatsis was glad to get Chamberlin. He had heard Captain Brown bellyache about him, but it had sounded more like sour grapes than anything else. He knew that Brown thought his CIB made him some sort of combat hero. And he sensed that Brown wished he had the balls to do what Chamberlin had done. He had also heard Captain White complain about Chamberlin's table manners and use of vulgarity. He did not know what those things had to do with being a good combat officer. Chamberlin was probably perceived as a threat to both Brown and White. Gatsis did not feel any threat from him.

As far as he was concerned, Chamberlin had conducted himself effectively while attached to his company. Though Chamberlin did not know it, he knew about Chamberlin's actions a few nights ago on Bethlehem Point. Word had spread about the man with the leather thongs. He knew of no one else who wore them. He had not said anything to him about it because he did not know exactly how to broach the subject. He thought maybe Chamberlin did not want anybody to know. Anyhow he knew Chamberlin had guts and he respected that.

He assigned Chamberlin to the third platoon. Sergeant Gunther was currently the acting platoon leader. He had recently led a very successful attack patrol against the Chinese at Luke's Castle. His patrol had surprised a large number of Chinese in some sort of group meeting. After he had skillfully positioned his men, they opened fire and slaughtered many of the enemy. For this action Sergeant Gunther had been recommended for a Silver Star and a battlefield commission. Gatsis thought Chamberlin and Gunther would get along well.

Perhaps they would have. They were not together long enough to find out.

The third platoon was occupying a ridge line to the southwest of Christmas Tree Ridge. They were farther away from the Chinese lines. An enemy attack was not very imminent there. They were somewhat isolated from the rest of the company.

Chamberlin introduced himself to Sergeant Gunther. He told him to carry on as he had been. He did not expect to be there long. He hoped his transfer to Japan would happen soon. So he did not want to usurp any of Gunther's authority over the platoon.

Gunther's CP was a fairly large bunker which accommodated about a half-dozen men. There was a wooden platform about a foot off the floor on which the men kept their things and slept. It had been built by and for Koreans who averaged a foot shorter than Americans. Therefore, if a six-footer stretched out on this platform bed, his feet would dangle over the edge. At one end of the bunker was an unplatformed space of about four by eight feet that seemed to be unoccupied.

Gunther offered Chamberlin room on the platform. Chamberlin declined. He did not want to take anyone's space. He put his things on the dirt floor at the end of the bunker.

Gunther and Chamberlin knew about each other. They were each somewhat in awe of the other. There was an unspoken, mutual respect between them. But Chamberlin was pissed off at having been transferred to a rifle platoon. He was not in a friendly mood. Gunther was not sure how he felt about Chamberlin taking over his platoon.

After a few moments of appraising his new quarters, Chamberlin borrowed a hatchet from one of the men. He went outside and cut some sturdy saplings into poles of the right length. He scrounged up some discarded commo wire and made a frame about seven by three feet. He took this inside the bunker and hung it from the log ceiling of the bunker with more wire. Then he wove more wire between the poles to form a sturdy bunk bed upon which to put his air mattress and sleeping bag. Soon his things were well organized. He had all the comforts of combat on the MLR.

The men in the bunker were surprised. Chamberlin had not asked anyone for help. They liked his bunk bed. The next day they all followed his example. They fashioned double-deck bunk beds along the walls of the bunker. This gave them much more room to organize their things and a more comfortable place to sleep.

Chamberlin inspected the ridge line his new platoon was responsible for. A long, shallow trench ran along the top of the ridge. The South Koreans not only slept on short beds, they also did not dig their defensive positions very deep. The task of the third platoon was to defend the ridge and dig deeper and better defensive positions. They were to rest and stay low during the day and stand guard and dig at night. It was winter and very cold. Chamberlin noticed that many of the men were sleeping on the bare, frozen ground with no overhead cover. His CP was the only bunker in the platoon area. Some of the men did not even have air mattresses. Though the mummy sleeping bags were good, they were not adequate in subzero temperatures. The men appeared numb and slowed down by the cold. *How the hell could they expect half-frozen zombies to fight, if need be, or to dig trenches in hard, frozen ground,* thought Chamberlin. From what he saw they had not done much digging so far.

Chamberlin had figured on just putting in his time in his new assignment until his transfer came through. He did not plan on making any waves or doing any more than he had to. He would let Gunther run the platoon. But the sight of these poor bastards freezing their asses off, with no one seeming to care, stirred his paternal instincts. They were now his men. It was up to him to take care of them. He had to figure out a way.

A few yards east of his CP was a spot where somebody had started digging a bunker into the bank before the ground froze. Chamberlin took a pickaxe and tested the strength of the frozen earth. He made a slight impression, but not much. It was frozen too solid. He gathered some firewood and built a fire to thaw the ground. One thing he had learned from his old man was how to build a fire in the woods.

"We aren't supposed to build any fires," Gunther warned Chamberlin. "We aren't even allowed to cut any trees without permission of the South Korean government."

"I know," replied Chamberlin. "But nobody can see a fire in the daylight, so nobody will know but us, will they? Tell the men they can come and get warm by shifts. Then they'll be able to work better at night."

Gunther did as he was told. He did not argue. He had made sure that Chamberlin knew the rules. That was all he could do.

Gradually, the men got warm. Gradually, the fire thawed the ground. That night Chamberlin threw caution to the winds. He built another bonfire to keep the men warm while they worked. They started excavating for a bunker. For the next few days and nights they dug and filled sandbags. Soon they had the walls up for a squad-size bunker.

Chamberlin requisitioned picks, shovels, and axes from supply. There were no questions asked as to why he needed them. No one from battalion or even company headquarters visited their positions.

Gunther was transferred and got his commission.

Chamberlin cut trees for logs for the roof of the new bunker. When it was finished, the men built bunk-beds and a squad moved in.

Things went so well with the first bunker that Chamberlin suspended work on the trenches. It was not amounting to much anyhow. He ordered the men to build two new bunkers so that all the men would be up off the ground and under cover. He made sure all the

189

men had air mattresses. He stationed lookouts at key spots along the ridge to warn of any enemy approach. Some of the men, especially the KATUSAs (Korean soldiers attached to U.S. forces) preferred standing guard to working, so they were given that choice.

One night Captain Gatsis called. "Battalion reports that somebody has got fires burning in your area," he said. "Is that you, Chamberlin?"

"Yes, Sir," admitted Chamberlin. "We have a small fire going to keep the men warm while they work. It's on the rear slope. I don't think the Chinese can see it."

"Well, you'll have to put it out," said Gatsis. "Battalion is very upset."

Chamberlin thought about the Turks, some of the fiercest fighters of the United Nations forces in this silly, stalemated conflict. They were famous for their large campfires, around which they sang and partied at night, as if defying the enemy to come out and fight. The Chinese seldom bothered them because of their fighting spirit. But he did not disobey Gatsis.

By now it did not matter too much. The platoon already had two bunkers with oil stoves inside for heat. Now Chamberlin had the men work a while on the new bunkers, then go into the other bunkers to get warm. The same for the KATUSA sentries.

Chamberlin had also noticed that the men and their clothes were very dirty when he arrived. Men that are numb with cold tend to neglect their personal hygiene. There was not much water on the MLR to wash with. And there had not been any way to heat what little there was. Cold men do not like to wash in cold water. To keep it from freezing, the water had been kept in the CP and rationed out sparingly.

Chamberlin knew about army field showers about a

mile behind the MLR. These were large tents housing showers. They had plenty of hot water. Soldiers could shower and swap their dirty clothes for clean. Either Gunther did not know about these facilities, or he had never been given permission to use them. It was probably low on the priority list of rear-echelon pencil-pushers who were warm and comfortable. Chamberlin took some of his men back to test the waters. No one at the showers asked any questions. So Chamberlin set up a schedule for showers. Half the men went back one day and the other half the next day. Chamberlin was not worried so much about the men being dirty. He just did not want them to suffer from the cold or get sick. Before he came, apparently, the men did not think they were allowed to leave the MLR. Maybe they were not. Chamberlin never checked to find out. He knew the Chinese never attacked during the day so he was not worried about carrying out his military mission. He did not need to ask permission to do what he thought was right for his men.

Within three weeks he had the warmest, best housed, cleanest platoon in the battalion. He wondered why others did less for their men.

Not long after Chamberlin was transferred to K Company, Major Morgan got his wish. Chamberlin's turn to take out a patrol came up.

Captain Gatsis was almost apologetic when he told Chamberlin he had patrol duty.

"I'm sorry, Chamberlin, but in fairness to my other officers," he said. "I know you've been through a lot already."

"That's okay," said Chamberlin. "I don't expect any special favors."

K Company had a peculiar way of selecting men for patrol duty. They did not want to leave any area unguarded by selecting a total unit—squad or platoon—so they picked men from different units to make up the patrol. The disadvantage of this system was that the men often did not know each other. They did not know if they could depend on the next guy or not. Taking a bunch of men, whom he did not know and who were strangers, on patrol was not exactly to Chamberlin's liking.

Their mission was simple enough. They merely had to go out a few hundred yards in front of Bethlehem Point and set up a listening post.

Chamberlin was not sure this was the best thing to do, but he took his small group into a bunker on Christmas Tree Ridge and explained very carefully to them the mission of the patrol. Then, from the roster, he ascertained meticulously each one's name. He had each man do the same. Each one memorized who was on the patrol, not necessarily their real names, but what each wanted to be called. Then he explained the order of march. Each man very carefully memorized the names of the men in front and back of him.

"Whatever you do," said Chamberlin, "stay in that order. If we get hit, don't panic and run. That's just what the enemy wants you to do. Then they can cut you down or capture you. You're safer to stay close together in the dark. Then you can help each other out."

They moved out shortly after dark. There was snow on the ground and it was cold. It was a clear night. The moon and stars were bright. They had no trouble maintaining contact and seeing where they were going. They were dressed warmly. Insulated Mickey Mouse boots kept their feet warm and dry. Heavy, fur-hooded parkas kept their bodies fairly comfortable. Their hands were protected by warm mittens with trigger fingers. It was not a difficult mission and conditions were all favorable.

But it was a long night. Time passed slowly. It was very quiet. After a few hours of huddling in the snow, Chamberlin became restless. He almost wished the Chinese would come. It would give him something to do. Maybe he could capture one. He wondered if there were any Chinese out there in that area. He made a snowball and threw it down the hill into some trees to see if he could arouse anyone. Nothing happened. He threw a few more. He did not scare up any enemy but he sure scared the hell out of the men. Was he insane?

Toward dawn they returned to the MLR.

In Luke's Castle the Chinese had loudspeakers over which they would broadcast to the American forces on Christmas Tree Ridge. At times they would play melancholy songs to remind the soldiers of home and their loved ones, hoping to make them homesick. At other times they would blare out propaganda about American imperialism, or fat, rich businessmen taking care of their wives and sweethearts back home.

A few days before Christmas of 1952, they started boasting that they would celebrate Christmas Eve by attacking Christmas Tree Ridge and bringing back many GI dogtags. They repeated this message over and over to drive fear into the hearts of the defenders.

The Chinese kept their word. On Christmas Eve they did attack. There was no warning artillery barrage. Shortly after dark, before friendly listening posts were posted, the enemy moved silently and swiftly across the short expanse of no-man's-land. They poured into the trenches, flinging their grenades, firing their rifles, and bayoneting the American troops. There was mass confusion and fighting. Chinese mixed with the Americans in fierce hand-to-hand combat. If not cut off by the enemy, some of the American forces tried to fall back. Many just hid in their bunkers.

When informed of the situation, Captain Gatsis left his CP and hurried toward Bethlehem Point, into the thick of the fray. He rallied his retreating troops and they fought the Chinese valiantly until finally the Chinese withdrew.

On Christmas Day Chamberlin's platoon took over the defense of Bethlehem Point. The men were apprehensive. Did the Chinese promise to attack on Christmas also? Would they come again tonight? Chamberlin wondered if his luck was running out. But the Chinese did not attack the next night, nor succeeding nights. A few days later the battalion was relieved and moved back to reserve positions.

One day Chamberlin was talking to Sergeant O'Leary about Captain Gatsis's courageous actions on Christmas Eve.

"He's been put in for a medal," said O'Leary.

Ever interested in brave deeds, and the awards granted for them, as a comparison to his own, Chamberlin asked, "What medal has he been recommended for?"

"The Medal of Honor," replied O'Leary seriously.

Chamberlin was surprised, as well as envious. *Was Gatsis's action so much greater than his, Browne's, Neathery's, Moroney's, or Pierce's?* He wondered. *Perhaps it was all in the writeups. Or would Van Fleet disapprove of it, as he had his DSC?*

However, despite his envy, Chamberlin had even greater respect for Captain Gatsis because of his heroism. Gatsis never spoke of his gallantry to Chamberlin.

20

Soon after the 179th Infantry moved off the MLR, orders came through transferring Chamberlin to Sasebo, Japan. He was to report on 13 January 1953.

Captain Gatsis shared the good news with him and paid him high praise for his service with K Company.

Captain Brown came to visit his friend, Andy Gatsis. Meeting Chamberlin was unavoidable because all of K Company's officers were quartered together.

"Hi, Al," Brown said in a low, meek voice.

"What the hell are you doing here?" Chamberlin responded sarcastically. "Where's your bodyguard? Aren't you afraid you might get hurt?"

"Let's have a drink and let bygones be bygones," suggested Brown.

"I don't drink with cowards," said Chamberlin.

No one in the large tent came to Brown's defense. They all pretended they did not hear. Chamberlin walked away from Brown.

On the journey south to Taegu from where he would board a flight to Sasebo, Chamberlin met Lieutenant Mello, who was going to Japan on R and R.

Mello had joined L Company after Chamberlin had left. He had taken over Chamberlin's second platoon. They had met briefly before on the MLR, but the contact had not been significant enough for Chamberlin to learn much about Mello.

However, Mello knew about Chamberlin. His men often talked of him. Chamberlin's popularity with the men had made him feel somehow inferior. He had felt he was competing with a legend that he could never live up to. He had learned of Chamberlin's recruiting volunteers for patrol duty from his platoon. That had irritated him. But he had also heard a lot of other things about Chamberlin that had impressed him, like bringing the girls into camp to service the men. Now that took balls.

"Chamberlin, let me shake your hand," said Mello excitedly. "I've always wanted to meet you. My name is Mello. My friends call me Mel. We met once up on the line, but you probably don't remember me."

"Yes, I remember," said Chamberlin. He was not sure he wanted to be friends with anyone connected to Captain Brown.

"Do you remember Kentucky, Partin, and Tally?" asked Mello. "They were always talking about you."

"Sure I remember them," said Chamberlin. "How could I ever forget them? They were damn good combat men."

"They sure are," agreed Mello. "Did you know that they were on the patrol with me when we captured a couple of Chinks down by the river?"

"I heard something about that," said Chamberlin. "Were you on that patrol?"

"Yeah, but those men deserve all the credit," said Mello. "They taught me a lot."

Chamberlin felt better about Mello now. He could not be too bad if he appreciated the value of his men.

"Say, is it true what they said about you?" asked Mello.

"I don't know," said Chamberlin. "What did they say?"

"They said you brought a couple geisha girls up to camp for the boys. Is that true?"

"I've never known those boys to lie," Chamberlin said evasively. He still was not sure how far he could trust Mello.

They traveled in silence for a while. Then Mello said, "Do geisha girls ever give blow jobs?"

The question surprised Chamberlin. Maybe Mello could be trusted after all.

"Some do and some don't," he replied.

"Boy, I wish I could get a good blow job," continued Mello.

"Well, we're stopping over night in Taegu," said Chamberlin. "Probably you could get one there."

"How would you find one?" asked Mello.

"Just go to a geisha house and ask," said Chamberlin.

"But how do you find a geisha house?" asked Mello.

"Oh they're all over the place," said Chamberlin. "I'll find one for you."

"Would you?" said Mello. "That's great. Say, can I call you Al?"

"Sure," said Chamberlin.

That issue settled, there was more silence.

Again Mello broke the ice. "But what if they don't want to give you a blow job?" he asked. "Do you just make them do it?"

"No, I wouldn't," replied Chamberlin. "You just let the mamasan know what you want and she'll find a girl that will do that for you. Just follow me. I'll show you."

"Boy, you're great," exclaimed Mello. "Everything they said about you is true. You're my hero."

"Thank you, but I don't imagine Captain Brown had anything good to say about me," answered Chamberlin.

"Oh that puny little bastard," said Mello. "Did you

know he never left his bunker while on the MLR, and that he had a personal bodyguard? He is a real prick."

"Yeah, I heard," said Chamberlin.

"Is it true that you tried to kill him?" asked Mello.

"No, that's not true," said Chamberlin. "I just scared him a little bit."

"That's not what Neathery said," countered Mello.

"Did you know Neathery?" asked Chamberlin. "I thought he rotated."

"He did," said Mello. "But he was the platoon sergeant when I joined the company in August. He rotated a little while after we went on line in November."

"He was a hell of a good combat soldier," said Chamberlin. "He was my hero. I learned a lot from him. Did he ever get his medals?"

"Yes, he got a Silver Star, but I heard that he had a DSC coming," said Mello. "I don't know if he ever got that."

"Did any of the other men I put in for medals ever get them?" asked Chamberlin.

"I don't know, but I don't think so," said Mellow. "Probably Brown screwed 'em out of 'em."

"Yeah, he probably did," agreed Chamberlin. "The son of a bitch!"

"I put Kentucky, Partin, and Tally in for medals for capturing those Chinks," said Mello. "I hope they get 'em."

"Did Neathery ever mention Bob Browne?" asked Chamberlin. "I put him in for the same medals as Neathery, a Silver Star and a DSC. He wrote me that he never got 'em yet."

"Yeah, the guys were always telling stories about you, Neathery, and Browne."

Mello and Chamberlin talked on and on during the

trip to Taegu. They had many things in common, not the least of which was their horniness.

In Taegu they checked in at their appointed billet. Then they set out in search of a good geisha house. This did not take long.

As promised, Chamberlin led the way. He told the mamasan what his new friend desired. None of the girls in the house were willing to perform fellatio, so she sent out for one that would. Like any good business person, she had a good supply system.

Chamberlin's needs were less specific. He picked the prettiest of the girls. They paid a little extra and spent the night. In the morning Mello appeared happy but drained.

They returned to their quarters, had breakfast, and boarded a plane for Sasebo.

Thus ended Chamberlin's tour of duty in Korea. On the plane he relaxed and half-dozed. On the edge between sleep and awareness, his thoughts drifted. He sure had been lucky. Combat in two wars without a scratch. His thoughts that he had had on Baldy, *if I ever get through this mess, I'll be able to face anything,* kept creeping into his ideation. He no longer planned to make the Army his career. He would finish out his three years and then return to freedom. His experiences with men like Brown and White had made him realize that, no matter what rank you might have, there would always be some prick that you would have to take orders from.

He was proud of what he had done in combat. He wondered if many officers had led as many men in such intense fighting for as long as he had with only three men killed. He thought maybe it was because they had fought so courageously. He thought it was safer to be brave than cowardly.

He now knew why he had had to come to Korea. It was to test his courage. It had been tested in World War II, but he had not received a definitive result then. Now the test results were decisive and positive. The conclusion was good. He was glad it was over.

But there was a nagging irritation that pestered him. Had he done enough to make sure his men got the medals they deserved for their heroism? He tried to rationalize that he had done all he could. But had he? Had he put his own selfish interest before all? At the time he had not thought he had. Guilt was defeated by rationalization.

Satisfied, he slept peacefully on the flight from Korea. As sleep deepened, a pleasant dream surfaced. All the heroes of his second platoon were lined up alphabetically. A pale, ghostly Captain Brown seemed to be crawling on his hands and knees in front of them. As he came to each one, he reached into a box of ashes and pulled out bright, shiny medals and handed them up to the men. The dream seemed to last a long time. Brown dug up the following medals for the following men:

Private Herman Bilke—two Bronze Stars
PFC Mason Bowman—two Bronze Stars
PFC Aden Boyd—two Bronze Stars
✷ Sergeant Robert Browne—Distinguished Service Cross, Silver Star, Bronze Star
PFC George Chalifour—Bronze Star
Corporal Harry Cottrell—two Bronze Stars
Sergeant James Crimmins—Bronze Star
PFC Melnie Dawes—Silver Star
PFC Carl Fields—Bronze Star
Sergeant Cecil Jackson—Silver Star, Bronze Star
PFC Walter Johnson—two Bronze Stars
Private Buddy June—Bronze Star

PFC Calvin Knox—two Bronze Stars
Corporal Roland Lincke—two Bronze Stars
Sergeant William McAfee—two Bronze Stars
Sergeant Jack Neathery—Distinguished Service Cross,
    Silver Star, Bronze Star
PFC Elroy Olson—two Bronze Stars
PFC John Partin—Bronze Star
PFC Jack Tally—Bronze Star
Sergeant Richard Webster—two Bronze Stars
Sergeant William West—Silver Star, Bronze Star

When he was finished, Captain Brown jumped into the box of ashes. Then he disappeared in a dusty puff. The line of decorated heroes joined hands and moved slowly into a strong tight circle.

A smile decorated the face of Chamberlin as he awoke somewhere over the Sea of Japan.